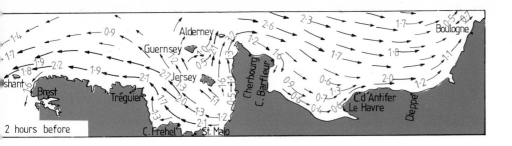

2 hours before

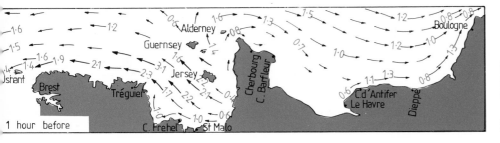

1 hour before

Mean rate of tidal streams in the Channel during the five hours leading up to HW DOVER.

Arrows indicate direction of the stream. The figures give average rate in knots at each point. For Spring rate, add one-third; at Neaps, subtract one-third of the figures shown on each chart.

For greater detail, see Admiralty Tidal Stream Atlases or relevant charts.

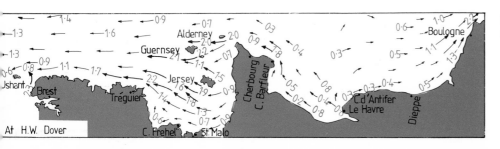

At H.W. Dover

The Shell Pilot to the English Channel

Revised by the same author

THE SHELL PILOT TO THE SOUTH COAST
HARBOURS

The Shell Pilot to the English Channel

2. Harbours in Northern France and the Channel Islands

Dunkerque to Brest

Captain J. O. Coote, Royal Navy

with plans by
James Petter

A Shell Guide

faber and faber
LONDON · BOSTON

First published in 1985
by Faber and Faber Limited
3 Queen Square London WC1N 3AU

Printed in Great Britain by
BAS Printers Limited, Over Wallop, Hampshire
All rights reserved

© Captain J. O. Coote, 1985

For
ANTONIA

British Library Cataloguing in Publication Data

Coote, J.O.
The Shell pilot to the English Channel.
Pt 2: Harbours in Northern France
and the Channel Islands
1. Pilot guides—English Channel
2. Harbours—English Channel
I. Title
623.89′2916336   VK839
ISBN 0-571-13486-6

CONTENTS

* Indicates that under certain conditions of wind or tide entry may be impracticable or potentially hazardous.

Part Five: NORTH-WEST BRITTANY

FOREWORD

This book is a companion volume to the *Shell Pilot to the South Coast Harbours* which covered those ports between Ramsgate and the Scillies considered suitable for a yacht drawing 2m0 to visit. In 1982 it was my privilege to revise that standard work on behalf of Adlard Coles, who first produced it before the War.

I now set out to cover from Dunkerque to Brest, including the Channel Islands. It was tempting to extend the scope of the book a little farther, because there happen to be very attractive deep-water ports just off either end—Ostend and Camaret. The former is a convenient place to leave one's boat, for a brief return to the office or to change crews, because London is a little over three hours away by jetfoil and boat-train. Camaret is the ideal place to wait for the tide to turn at the Raz de Sein or Chenal du Four. It offers pontoon berths and waterfront bistros geared to the tastes of cruising yachtsmen.

With two exceptions all the pictures accompanying the text are hitherto unpublished. They were commissioned by me and taken during the nine-months' field-work period which began in July 1983. After weeks of waiting for the right weather, the whole aerial survey was completed in three days by Malcolm Knight and Graham Adams of Sealand Aerial Photography, Chichester, using respectively a Cessna 172 and a Hasselblad ELM, both about the right speed for the job. Nearly all the sea-level shots were taken by my daughter, Belinda Coote, mostly in the rain during bitterly cold, short winter days. She used an Olympus OM1 with 35–70mm lens and usually 400 ASA film, which literally made light of the discouraging environment. I shot dozens of reels along the whole route, but ended up only being able to claim most of the Channel Islands pictures in Part Four as my own. Credits are given wherever a picture was *not* taken by Sealand, my daughter or myself.

Once again, the simplified harbour plans have been drawn with care and distinction by James Petter of Petersfield.

I am also greatly indebted to friends who have put all or parts of my manuscript to the test of their local knowledge and literacy: Air Vice-Marshal Bill Crawford-Compton, Lt.-Commander Os de Las Casas, Elizabeth Dorey, Admiral Sir John Fieldhouse, Major-General Jim Gavin, Anne Parker (who also typed the whole book), Baron Danny Pouget, Donald Thompson and Rear-Admiral Sir John Woodwood. At every port I found the local harbour masters helpful, if a little uncomprehending in the remoter backwaters of Brittany. Captain Roy Bullen, the Harbour Master at St Helier, was especially patient. So was my wife, without whose help with the research and administration underlying this considerable project it would never have seen the light of day.

Obviously I have been at pains to ensure that the most up-to-date and accurate data has gone to the printers, based on many sources and verified by my own observations. I am indebted to the Controller, HM Stationery Office, the Hydrographer of the Navy, the Service Hydrographique et Océanographique de la Marine (SHOM), the Éditions Cartographiques Maritimes (Navicartes) and Imray Laurie Norie and Wilson Ltd, for allowing me to refer to their charts and publications as part of the source-material where applicable. At the head of the section on each port I have listed the charts recommended for use with my text and harbour plans as the most reliable guides to safe navigation. Those shown in brackets are more suitable for making passage to the harbour approaches, rather than for entry or departure.

My aim has been to whet the appetite of the keelboat owner who has not yet discovered the wild, seductive beauty of the whole nor'west coast of France in all its moods. Originally I intended to limit the choice of harbours covered to those which a boat drawing 1m8 could sail right into and, after a brief wait in good shelter, reach an alongside berth. But I soon found that, the major commercial ports apart, I should have been writing a very slim book indeed. So I have included some half-tide stop-overs which I have found to be worth the diversion, as the *Guide Michelin* would put it. The list is entirely subjective, and I make no apologies for its omissions.

No matter how much care and attention is lavished on achieving accuracy, mistakes will emerge or evolve with the passage of time. Hence the cautionary waiver given such prominence by my publisher's lawyers. Please write and tell me if you have any corrections or constructive criticisms: c/o Faber and Faber Ltd, 3 Queen Square, London WC1N 3AU.

John Coote
July 1984

PART ONE

GENERAL INFORMATION

Terms and notations, abbreviations, conversion tables,
radio and weather, French–English glossary

CROSS-CHANNEL DISTANCES

Safe navigable routes between breakwaters and/or estuary entrances (in nautical miles)

	NORTH FORELAND	DUNGENESS	BEACHY HEAD	NAB TOWER	NEEDLES	ANVIL POINT	PORTLAND BILL	BERRY HEAD	RAME HEAD	LIZARD	BISHOP ROCK
BOULOGNE	39	25	51	97	125	137	157	196	227	269	318
DIEPPE	90	58	58	91	115	126	144	182	211	246	294
LE HAVRE LV	130	96	75	76	88	94	106	140	165	198	246
GRANDCAMP	158	122	94	78	80	82	89	116	140	175	223
CHERBOURG	164	128	98	66	60	57	60	84	106	141	188
ALDERNEY	180	144	114	74	61	53	49	65	85	118	167
ST PETER PORT	201	165	134	96	83	73	65	70	90	112	157
ST HELIER	219	183	151	113	101	94	87	94	108	130	173
ST MALO	245	209	178	140	127	120	113	117	138	145	183
LÉZARDRIEUX	243	207	175	134	123	113	102	92	100	108	146
MORLAIX	274	238	206	169	149	138	124	106	100	92	123
L'ABER-WRAC'H	300	264	231	195	171	159	146	117	103	84	104
LE CONQUEST	325	289	252	216	192	179	161	136	120	98	110
BREST	342	306	269	233	209	196	178	153	137	115	127

Layout   The ports covered are dealt with from east to west (Dunkerque to Brest) with the Channel Islands and adjacent coast of France between the Normandy and North-West Brittany sections.

Charts and Conventions   Nearly all the 52 ports have their own simplified harbour plans specially drawn for this book to the approximate scale shown on each. These plans should not be relied upon for navigation; they are a simplified version of the best data available from several sources including my own observation. To assist yachtsmen select the best charts available, their publisher and listed numbers are shown at the head of each port. The most suitable are usually of a scale of 15,000:1 or less. The least useful are given in brackets. Their origins are abbreviated as follows:

BA   British Admiralty chart by the Hydrographer of the Navy
FR   French Navy chart by Service Hydrographique et Océanographique de la Marine (SHOM)
Stan   Stanfords Coloured charts by Barnacle Marine Ltd
Im   Imray Laurie Norie and Wilson Ltd
CG   Carte Guide de Navigation Côtière by Éditions Cartographiques Maritimes (Navicarte)

The last three are the handiest: they have concertina-folds in the manner of road-maps. Those issued by the two navies are delivered with a single fold usually 110 × 50 cm (about 43 × 20 in). The choice of those to have on board will be determined partly by their scale and legibility, but also on the basis of what individual yacht navigators feel most comfortable with. Familiarity with French Navy charts is not an easily acquired taste for British sailors; there is the language problem, and their style, presentation and symbols are significantly different.

For planning purposes it is best to have a general chart(s) covering the whole Channel (BA 2675 or Stan 1 and 2). Then, considering the cost of charts and their short shelf life, shop around. An unused chart would buy a gourmet meal in France.

Distances   are given in nautical miles (n.m.) and cables (200yds) at sea; in kilometres and metres on land. (See conversion table p. 18.) The range of lights is shown by 'M' after numerals indicating its nominal range in nautical miles.

Heights   are given in metres. Against a light's characteristics its height above sea level is given by numerals with the suffix 'm'. Thus 36m 19M is a light 36 metres above sea level with a nominal range of 19 nautical miles. Conspicuous objects ashore may have their heights indicated by numerals in brackets.

Bearings and Courses   are True, to which local magnetic Variation should be added (5½°W in the Straits of Dover to 8°W off Brest) and Deviation (if any) applied for ship's magnetic compass readings. Unless otherwise stated all bearings of shore points mentioned in the text are *from seaward*.

Times of High Water   For each port the average time difference is given relevant to HW Dover and to the nearest Standard Port (SP). Nearly every port has its own local tide-tables usually available free from a chandlery or Harbour Office, which may be more precise. All times are based on GMT or the time prevailing at the SP.

Heights above Chart Datum   are given in metres and centimetres for Springs and Neaps at Mean High Water (MHW) and Mean Low Water (MLW). To be more precise consult Admiralty Tide Tables, but even then tide levels can vary significantly due to strong winds persisting for any length of time from the same quarter.

Chart Notations—Lights and Buoys

Some of the characteristics used in this book in two languages:

English	Characteristic	French
F	Fixed	Fixe, Fx, or F
Fl	Flashing	é
LFl	Long Flash	él
Oc	Occulting	Occ
Q	Quick Flashing	Scint or sc
Fl(2) 3s	Group Flash (2) every 3s	F2é (3s)
W	White	b
R	Red	r
G	Green	v
Vi	Violet	vi
Bu	Blue	bl
Y	Yellow	j
B	Black	N
Grey	Grey	Gris
Or	Orange	Or
Iso	Isophase	Iso
Alt	Alternating	Alt
Oc (1 + 2) WG 12s	Composite Group Occulting 1 eclipse followed by 2 White Green every 12 seconds	F.20.10(12s) bv
Ø Lts . . . (degs)	Lights in transit	2 Feux à . . . (degs)

Note that in giving the colours of lights the French use small letters (e.g. 'r' 'v' for RG) but in describing buoys or light structures their colours are indicated by capital letters. Thus an N-cardinal buoy (BY) would be 'NJ' and a BRB isolated danger mark 'NRN'.

French–English Glossary

(excluding the obvious—*quai, jetée, môle, île*, etc)

Navigation Marks

phare	lighthouse
radiophare	radio beacon
klaxon or typhon	horn
cloche (cl)	bell
sifflet (s)	whistle
balise	beacon
charpente pyl.	lattice tower
tour or tourelle	tower
à damier	chequered
voy.	topmark
los.	diamond
carré	square
cyl	round
falaise	cliff
flèche	spire
épave	wreck
marques cardinales	cardinal buoys
marques latérales	lateral buoys
à bâbord	to port
à tribord	to starboard
sens conventionel	buoyage direction
échelle	scale

Harbours and Approaches

amer	landmark
anse	bay
asséchage	drying berth
échouage	beaching
barre	bar

brise-lames	breakwater
basse mer	low water
pleine mer	high water
marée	tide
vive-eau	spring tide
morte eau	neap tide
étale	slack water
flot	flood tide
jusant	ebb tide
terre-plein	levelled ground
cale	slipway
chenal	channel
darse	basin
digue	mole or breakwater
bassin à flot	wet basin
grue	crane
mouillage	anchorage
bouée	buoy
grève	sandy beach
galets	shingle
écluse	lock-gates
douane	customs

Other Abbreviations Used and French Equivalents

TG	Digital Tide Gauge
HM	Harbour Master (Capitainerie)
HA	Harbour Authority (Affaires Maritimes)
HO	Harbour or Marina Office (Bureau du Port)
Yacht Hbr	Marina (Port de Plaisance)
YC	Yacht Club (Club Nautique, Cercle Nautique)
SC	Sailing Club ('Voile' suffix)
FW	Fresh Water (eau douce)
Fuel	Petrol or diesel (carburant)

Ⓥ Visitors berths (Apportement visiteurs) or (places réservées au passage)

→| Right hand edge (le tombant droite)

|← Left hand edge (le tombant gauche)

SP Standard port—for tides.

Traffic Signals in use in French Ports With the advent of high-density lights, flags and shapes are gradually being replaced. For most ports other than the major ones, the 'simplified' system is in use. Sometimes, as in opening swing-bridges or lock-gates, ordinary road traffic lights are used, which are self-explanatory.

	SIMPLIFIED SYSTEM		NORMAL SYSTEM	
	DAY	NIGHT	DAY	NIGHT
No Entry	▮ R	● R	● B ▲ B ● B	● R ○ W ● R
No departure	▮ G	● G	▼ B ▲ B ▼ B	● G ○ W ● G
Neither way permitted	▮ R ▮ G	● R ● G	▼ B ▲ B ● B	● G ○ W ● R
Emergency Port shut	● R ● R ● R	● R ● R ● R	SAME	
Port open—Navigate with care	Code Flags	● G ● G ● G	SAME	

15

Depth and Tidal Signals Shown in a Few Major Ports

		DAY	NIGHT
Tide Rising	▲	B	● G ○ W
High Water	⊠	W B cross	○○ W
Tide Falling	▼	B	○ W ● G
Low Water	⚑	Bu	●● G

Depth Above Datum Shown by 3 Hoists in Parallel
(from l to rt)

KEY:

B ▼ or ● G Lt	B ■ or ● R Lt	B ● or ○ W Lt
per om 2	*per 1m 0*	*per 5m 0*

EXAMPLES

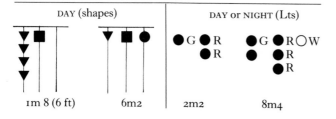

DAY (shapes)		DAY or NIGHT (Lts)	
1m 8 (6 ft)	6m2	2m2	8m4

Special Signals   Some of the major commercial ports also use supplementary signals to indicate movements by very large ships, those with special cargoes or ferries. If in doubt keep out of the way. It is always best to enter or leave a busy port under power—many insist that you should do so. On arrival at any major port get a copy of the local by-laws. Otherwise keep in mind Rule 9(b) of the International Regulations for Preventing Collisions at sea:

> A vessel of under 20m in length or a sailing vessel shall not impede the passage of a vessel which can safely navigate only within a narrow channel or fairway.

Weather Forecasts   In addition to the BBC shipping forecasts put out at 0033, 0555, 1355, 1750 daily, on British time Radio 4 200kHz or 1500m, there are numerous local forecasts, applicable mainly to the English coast. BBC's long wave can be ready easily throughout the area covered by this book.

The French reporting areas from Dunkerque to Brest (with equivalent British areas):

No. 9	Sandettie	(Dover area)
No. 10	Manche Est	(Wight)
No. 11	Manche Ouest	(Portland and Plymouth)
No. 12	Ouest Bretagne	(N Biscay)

These areas are all covered on Radio France Allouis long-wave transmissions in French on 164kHz (1820m) at 0725 and 1850 GMT. Also Radio France on 1071kHz (170m) in West Brittany. During the Summer there are special small craft forecasts as well. There are eight local VHF forecasts within the area covered by the book. They are noted in the text for the ports concerned. Boulogne and Brest mention wave forecasts on 1771 and 1673kHz at 0703 and 1733.

VHF Frequencies   The universal calling and safety frequency is Channel 16 (156.800MHz calling) which must never be cluttered by routine traffic. Most merchantmen and all warships and warships and coastal stations keep a listening watch on it, so it is permissible to call a ship on sighting, but be ready to switch to a working frequency. Here is a list of VHF channels and frequencies used as working frequencies by shore stations:

Ch 1	160.650MHz	Calais
2	160.700	Dieppe St Malo
3	160.750	Port-en-Bessin
9	156.450	Generally used by marina offices
10	156.500	
11	156.550	Honfleur
12	156.600	Widely used for port control
13	156.650	
14	156.700	
23	156.150	Boulogne Le Havre
24	161.800	Dunkerque Dieppe Ushant
25	161.850	Boulogne
26	161.900	Brest/Le Conquet
27	161.950	Cherbourg
28	162.000	Le Havre Brest/Le Conquet
37	157.850	(Marina band)
61	160.675	Dunkerque
67	156.375	(UK Coastguards)
68	156.425	Ouistreham
82	161.725	Le Havre Ushant
83	156.175	Plougasnou (Morlaix Bay)
84	161.825	Paimpol
87	161.975	Calais
88	162.025	Calais VHF Rdo Lt.Ho.

Radio (R/T or Rdo D/F)

Morse Code and Phonetic Alphabet

A	· —	Alfa
B	— · · ·	Bravo
C	— · — ·	Charlie
D	— · ·	Delta
E	·	Echo
F	· · — ·	Foxtrot
G	— — ·	Golf
H	· · · ·	Hotel
I	· ·	India
J	· — — —	Juliet
K	— · —	Kilo
L	· — · ·	Lima
M	— —	Mike
N	— ·	November
O	— — —	Oscar
P	· — — ·	Papa
Q	— — · —	Quebec
R	· — ·	Romeo
S	· · ·	Sierra
T	—	Tango
U	· · —	Uniform
V	· · · —	Victor
W	· — —	Whisky
X	— · · —	X-Ray
Y	— · — —	Yankee
Z	— — · ·	Zulu
é	· · — · ·	

DEPTH CONVERSION SCALE.   Fathoms & Feet ── Metres & Decimetres

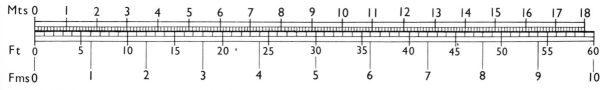

Conversion Factors (one place of decimals)

n.m	Km	n.m	Km
1	1.9	8	14.8
2	3.7	9	16.7
3	5.6	10	18.5
4	7.4	20	37.0
5	9.3	30	55.6
6	11.1	40	74.1
7	13.0	50	92.6

metres	ft/ins.	metres	ft/ins.
0.1	4″	0.8	2′7″
0.2	8″	0.9	2′11″
0.3	1′0″	1.0	3′3″
0.4	1′4″	1.2	3′11″
0.5	1′8″	1.4	4′7″
0.6	2′0″	1.6	5′3″
0.7	2′4″	1.8	5′11″

Planning for a Cruise to France There is an admirable booklet, *RYA Cruising* C1/84 Vol. 1, which gives plain guidance so as not to be caught with your documents down on cruising to France. It is available from: Royal Yachting Association, Victoria Way, Woking, Surrey, GU21 1EQ (tel: 04862-5022). The French Government Tourist Office at 178 Piccadilly, London, W1V 0AL (tel: 01-491-7622) is also worth contacting, preferably by a personal visit.

Before departure

(a) Check crews each have *passports*—they may never be called for unless any of them visits a casino, wants to use a Eurocheque card at a bank or return to UK independently.

(b) *Clear UK customs* by filling in Part 1 of Form C 1328, obtainable from any Customs House and at most UK marinas.

(c) Unless you are an officially registered British ship and hold *ship's papers* in a hardback cover, you can always put your boat on the Small Ships' Register. It only costs a tenner and can be obtained quickly through the RYA.

(d) Have a British ensign, a French flag for the starboard yardarm, and a 'Q' flag to be shown until cleared by French customs and police (immigration). In practice, even at large ports of entry like Cherbourg, let alone small ones like Barfleur, you may have difficulty in finding anyone to pay the slightest attention to your arrival—except the man collecting harbour/berthing dues and possibly the agent for duty free stores.

Cautionary Notes Many harbours listed in the remainder of the book have restricted access due to tide or weather. They are prefixed by an asterisk both in the Contents and on the chapter heading. The text following will make the dangers apparent.

Times quoted for opening and shutting of lock-gates may vary according to the tidal range (or 'coefficient', as the French say). If in doubt call the local harbour master on the telephone number listed. You will seldom be wrong if you show up at the lock-gates half an hour before local HW. Above all, don't bring back a pet or stray animal from France, unless you are prepared to face the stiff quarantine regulations governing their entry.

PART TWO

PAS DE CALAIS — SOMME

Dunkerque — St Valery-sur-Somme

including the main ferry ports for day-trippers, retreating armies
and invasion forces who hesitate too long while weighing up
the odds of making it to Kent

Soundings and heights in metres
Bearings and courses in degrees true
Distances at sea in nautical miles or cables

Safe navigable distances from breakwater to breakwater or fairway buoys (in nautical miles)

	RAMSGATE	DUNKERQUE	CALAIS	BOULOGNE	LE TOUQUET/ÉTAPLES	ST VALÉRY/LE CROTOY	BRIGHTON
RAMSGATE							
DUNKERQUE	39						
CALAIS	27	20					
BOULOGNE	37	41	20				
LE TOUQUET/ÉTAPLES	48	51	32	12			
ST VALÉRY/LE CROTOY	66	69	50	30	19		
BRIGHTON	81	96	78	65	67	71	

1   DUNKERQUE

Charts   *BA 1350 ; Fr 6500 ; Im C30 ; (CG 1010 ; Stan 1)*
High Water   *+00h 50 Dover   SP Dunkerque*
Heights above Datum   *Springs   MHW 5m8   MLW 0m6*
                           Neaps   MHW 4m8   MLW 1m5

DUNKERQUE is remembered by our generation for the miraculous deliverance in May 1940 of 340,000 troops, one-third of them across open beaches to the E of the town. It was not the first time the port had had an Army waiting to be taken off. In 1588 the Duke of Medina Sidonia's fleet was caught off Calais because, with their deep draught, his ships were unable to navigate through the shoals to their rendezvous with the Duke of Parma's invasion army in Dunkerque.

Pictures taken in 1940 and the town's earlier fame as the home port of the famous corsair Jean-Bart in Louis XIV's day do not prepare one for the shock of first sailing into the harbour today. It is now France's third port, handling ships up to 300,000 tons on its 12 miles of quaysides. It has a vast industrial complex spewing smoke over the western side of the town, and a major shipyard to the east.

All this and most of today's city of 85,000 inhabitants have been built since the war. Hence the inevitable name of the massive locks leading from the Avant-Port to the endless succession of commercial docks—Charles de Gaulle.

In the middle of it all, opposite the shipyard, and within walking distance of downtown Dunkerque, there are three local YCs each with its own pontoon berths, just 45 miles from Ramsgate, accessible at all states of the tides and perfectly sheltered.

Approaches

From the West   Pick up the Dunkerque Lanby Light buoy

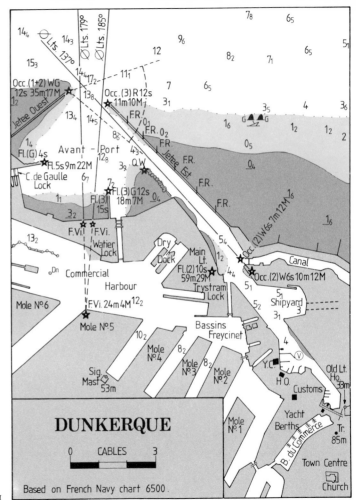

DUNKERQUE

CABLES

Based on French Navy chart 6500.

1.1   West jetty lighthouse.

4 miles N of the entrance to Calais. This is a 10m-high R tubular structure on a flat circular buoy with a 25M Fl 3s light and a continuous Radio Beacon, callsign "DK" on 294.2kHz with a notional 10M range. Its fog signal is (3) 60s. This buoy is ½ mile ENE of the R Dyck buoy—Fl R (2) 6s.

Head 100° for 2½ miles to pick up the first of fifteen pairs of Fl R and G buoys. R cans are even-numbered starting DW2 to port: G pillars, odd-numbered to starboard from DW1 to DW29 outside the entrance to Dunkerque harbour.

This channel (Passe de l'Ouest) is 15 miles long and in places only 3 cables wide. It has a least depth of 11.5m, but there are graveyard shoals on either side for most of the passage.

Between DW9 and 11 you pass 2 miles off Gravelines. Leaving DW15 to starboard you are right outside Dunkerque Ouest.

From the East   Pass 3½ miles off Nieuport towards the West Diep and the Passe de Zuydcoote and leave to port on a SW'ly course the Nieuport Bank buoy (YBY pillar with W-cardinal topmark, (Q (9) 15s)); 4 miles farther on course 235° is the first of the E channel buoys (S-cardinal Q (6) 10s). It is No.E12. The six odd-numbered buoys to be left to port start with E11 8 cables south of E12. Course 210° hits off the narrowest part of the channel, south of Banc Hills between E8 and E7. Note that E10 is the only one without a light.

Here course is altered to 260° (leaving all the R buoys to starboard) to pick up the G pillar E1 buoy with cone topmark and Lt Fl (2) G 6s. The harbour entrance is 1½ miles course 245° from here.

Harbour Entrance   In following all the foregoing and especially when approaching the entrance to the Avant-Port, the tidal stream runs ENE across your course at up to 3½ knots at springs, starting 2½ hours before HW Dunkerque (−01h 40 on HW Dover). The WSW tide starts 3½ hours after local HW (+04h 15 Dover). Going through the entrance leave to starboard the W jetty lighthouse 35m high (Oc (1+2) WG 12s with a range of

1.2   East jetty showing red lights along breakwater and main town lighthouse on the right. Entrance for yachts is between these points.

1.3   Another view of the lighthouse from the yacht club de la Mer du Nord pontoons opposite the shipyard.

1.4 Visitors' berths at the yacht club on outboard end of pontoons.

17M). The tower stands 35m above the sea and looks like a pepper grinder fitted with three flat flanges just below the part carrying the light (pic 1.1). It is listed as a W tower, but the stonework has aged and it looks more terra cotta. Its fog signal is (1 + 2) 60s. Standard light traffic signals are shown here (see p. 15).

The E jetty-head light (pic 1.2) is less impressive—just a W metal lattice tower with a R top, a mere 11m off the sea. Its light is Oc (3) R 12s and has a range of 10M. Foghorn (3) 30s.

There is an unusual arrangement of FVi lights to help the big ships making the entrance on the correct course of 182°. They may be of help to check that the tide is being correctly offset. The rear light lines up with two forward ones having intensified transits on 185° and 179° respectively.

The most impressive and conspicuous landmark is the 59m high W lighthouse 8 cables SE of the harbour entrance. Its light is Fl (2) 10s with a range of 29 miles. It lies on the W bank of the old port, the only one of interest to visiting yachtsmen. Directly opposite, on the E bank, is the entrance to the Wateringues Canal with leading lights at its entrance, each Oc (2) 6s on W columns with R tops, lined up to 137°, the course a visitor should now be taking up-harbour.

VHF contact can be made on Ch16 or 12.

Berthing and Facilities Just beyond the shipyard there is the first Yacht Hbr, which has 250 alongside berths. It is the property of the Yacht Club de la Mer du Nord, a hospitable little clubhouse on the west bank with a least depth at its berths of

1.5   The hospitable yacht club de la Mer du Nord.

1.6   Old lighthouse beyond the yacht club with fishing club berths just around the corner to starboard.

1.7 Sizeable keelboats in the Bassin du Commerce, only accessible through a lock and two swing-bridges.

3m85. Visitors should secure on the outside of the pontoon running parallel to the shore and farthest out (pics 1.3, 1.4 and 1.5).

FW, diesel and electricity all available. There are full repair and chandlery facilities. There is a gridiron and a 4½-ton crane.

Telephone number for the administration is (28) 66–79–90, while the clubhouse is on (28) 66–17–84. Weather forecasts on (28) 67–03–46.

The main Harbour Board offices are next door, and customs a block farther away: tel. (28) 66-96-64.

Weather on tape (28) 65-03-46 or on VHF Ch61 at 0633 and 1133 (Area 9 Sandettie).

There are more pontoon berths farther upstream, but not of immediate use to visitors. The Fishing Club's berths are where

this arm of the harbour ends with a causeway linking dockland with the centre of town (pic 1.6). There are yacht berths on pontoons in the Bassin du Commerce, but yachts can only get in or out through a succession of locks as part of the commercial docks area (pic. 1.7).

From the YC it is a quarter of a mile's walk to the heart of town, with all the amenities of a prosperous commercial and industrial city.

Communications   Unless you want to drive to Paris, in which case the start of the autoroute is only 10km south, travel is not easy. The E–W roads are hard work—the nearest ferries (to Dover or Ramsgate) are at Dunkerque Ouest, 5km away. There is no near-by airport.

2 CALAIS

Charts   *BA 1352 ; Fr 6474 ; Im C30 ; (CG 1010 ; Stan 1)*
High Water   *+ooh 25 Dover   SP Calais*
Heights above Datum   *Springs   MHW 6m8   MLW 0m7*
                                     Neaps   MHW 5m5   MLW 2m0

JUST 21 miles across the Straits of Dover Calais is the nearest French port to England. Indeed, for two centuries up to 1558 it was part of England, which might justify a parallel claim to those demanding sovereignty over the Falklands or Gibraltar, unless the wishes of 80,000 inhabitants were held to be 'paramount'.

The links with England go beyond 140 daily ferry movements in the summer which handle over six million tourists. Here in 1588 Drake's fireships panicked the Spanish Armada into the wastes of the North Sea and oblivion. In the First World War it was uncomfortably close to the front line, but did not fall into German hands until the Second World War, in May 1940, after a stubborn, sacrificial rearguard action by the Green Jackets stopped the panzers from rushing Dunkerque from the west.

For nearly 200 years it has been the centre of the lace industry, brought to Calais from Nottingham.

Rodin's famous statue of the *Six Burghers of Calais*, who saved the population from being put to the sword by Edward III in 1347, is in the park in front of the colourful gingerbread baroque Town Hall, faintly reminiscent of St Pancras station.

Gales from NW–NE across the sandbanks can make the entrance very uncomfortable, but inside, the Bassin de l'Ouest has the whole of its right-hand quay over 600m long functioning as a secure yacht harbour.

For the best all-round view climb the 271 steps to the top of

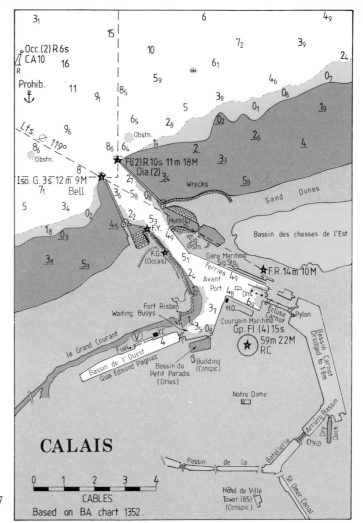

CALAIS

Based on BA chart 1352.

2.1   Entrance from seaward. Note new Harbour and Traffic Control Office (A). Yacht harbour is off to right of picture.

2.2   Ruins of Fort Risban on right; 1848 lighthouse on left. The yacht is about to pick up one of the waiting moorings outside the yacht harbour.

2.3 View of yacht harbour in Bassin de l'Ouest from the swing-bridge.

the old lighthouse in the heart of town, midway between the ferry terminals and the marina.

Approaches There is a bank (Ridens de la Rade) running parallel to the shore up to one mile off. Its least depth of 0m5 at LW springs effectively discourages any direct inshore approach from the east, except on the top half of the tide and when it is not blowing from the NE–NW. Then it can be imprudent to enter at all.

The safest bet is to lay off a course to a point a mile W of the town and make your landfall on the R can bell buoy CA8 with a QR light, leave it to port and head 095° for the entrance a mile away. A safe bearing of 110° on the town's most prominent light holds good all the way to the English coast 22 miles away. The light is Fl (4) 15s from an octagonal W tower 51m high. It

has a 20M Radio Beacon callsign "CS" on 305.7kHz. Also emanating from the lighthouse there is a VHF Radio Beacon on Ch88 (162.025kHz callsign "CL" 20M range) serving as Rdo. Lt. Ho.

As always in these parts the need to remember tidal currents in determining courses made good is paramount. Off the entrance the ENE stream starts $3\frac{1}{2}$ hours before HW Dover, while it turns WSW 3 hours after HW Dover. The maximum rate at springs is nearly 3 knots.

The outer ends of the two breakwaters forming the entrance are marked as follows:

E head: Wooden tower, R top, 10m high. Light Fl (2) R 10s 20M. The fog signal is (2) 40s.

W head: W tower, G top 12m 8M. The light is Iso G 3s. The fog signal is a bell ev 5s.

29

2.4   Marina office with all club facilities.

By night a transit of the latter with the intensified FR 14M Lt at the Gare Maritime on 118° is a useful guide. By day it is better to come in on a 138° transit of the W jetty head with the Town's main light (see above).

It is obligatory to enter and leave under power and to keep out of the way of all commercial traffic (pic. 2.1).

About 3 cables inside the entrance the fairway narrows. The ferries haul off to port to their RO/RO terminals. Yachts should alter slowly round the abandoned Fort Risban towards the lock-gates in front of the Bassin de l'Ouest (pic. 2.2).

Berthing and Facilities   The HM and port traffic control are now housed in a prominent, grey-slate three-storeyed building with one sloping side situated on the knuckle on the E bank of the narrowest part of the fairway. Light signals in accordance with the Normal System govern traffic movement.

VHF on Ch12.

There are eight R mooring buoys laid right outside the lock and bridge, intended for yachts to await the rather infrequent opening times, which are for a few minutes 2h and 1h before HW and 1h afterwards.

An Or light at the lock is a 10-min warning. G means go; R forbids all movements. The precise times are posted at the lock-keeper's office and in the Yacht Hbr clubhouse.

Inside the basin, where there is a least depth of 3m5, visitors can pick up any available berth on the right-hand side of the basin and then report to the office within the building, which has all the facilities of a YC, but is not so designated. The YC du Nord de la France has boat parking facilities in the old Fort, but not much else (pics 2.3 and 2.4).

The Yacht Hbr has FW, diesel, electricity and a crane for boat storage: tel. (21) 34–55–23.

The Customs are on: (21) 34–75–40.

Weather reports from Boulogne: tel. (21) 31–79–90, or VHF Ch87 at 0633 and 1133. Area 9 Sandettie.

Communications   Ferries to Dover and Folkestone. Hovercraft to Dover. SNCF to Paris.

3 BOULOGNE

Charts *BA 438 ; Fr 6436 ; Im C30 ; CG 1011 ; (Stan 1)*
High Water *—00h 07 Dover SP Boulogne*
Heights above Datum *Springs MHW 9m0 MLW 0m9*
  Neaps MHW 7m0 MLW 2m7

ALTHOUGH only 4 miles farther from Dover than Calais, Boulogne has surprisingly lagged behind as a tourist attraction, with 3,500,000 visitors a year. The thirteenth-century walled town dominating the city has as its centrepiece the Notre Dame Cathedral built in the mid-nineteenth century to replace one laid waste by the revolutionaries. It is on the site where a vision of Our Lady was claimed in the seventh century.

It was the jumping-off point for two invasions of England,

3.1 (A) Note north breakwater mostly submerged, so as to reduce tidal current across entrance. Yachts follow the same route inward as car ferries.

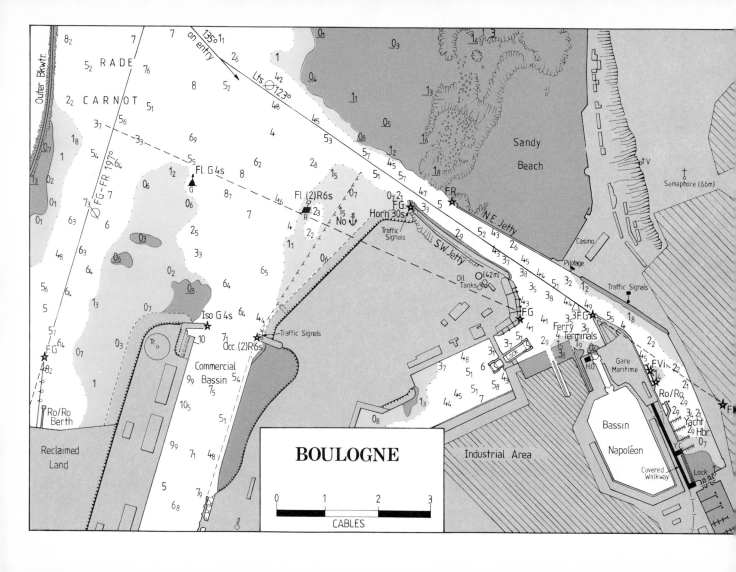

BOULOGNE

CABLES

0 1 2 3

RADE
CARNOT

Outer Bkwtr.

Sandy
Beach

Semaphore (66m)

FG · FR 197°

Fl.G 4s

Fl (2)R 6s

No

Horn 30s

Traffic
Signals

Traffic Signals

S.W. Jetty

N.E. Jetty

F.G.

FR

Casino

Pilotage

Oil
Tanks

(42m)

Iso G 4s

Tr.

Occ.(2)R 6s

Traffic Signals

FG

Ro/Ro
Berth

Reclaimed
Land

Commercial
Bassin

FG

F.FG

3.FG

Ferry
Terminals

LOCK

HO

Gare
Maritime

F.Vi

Ro/Ro

Yacht
Hbr.

F.R

Industrial Area

Bassin
Napoléon

Covered
Walkway

Lock

3.2   *Head of south mole (Carnot).*

3.3   *Head of north mole.*

which never got beyond assembling all the troops in readiness, led by Julius Caesar and Napoleon Bonaparte—to name but two. Napoleon left a reminder in the shape of a Column 143m high on the skyline dedicated to his Grand Army.

Today it is France's most active fishing port.

The outer harbour (Rade Carnot) is over 4 square miles in area. For the most part it is dedicated to commercial traffic. The only home for yachts is in the Port de Marée just beyond the RO/RO ferry terminals and Gare Maritime, where there are pontoon berths for 90 boats.

Approaches   From the W there are virtually no off-lying dangers once across the E-going main shipping lane. Away to the NE Cap Gris-Nez shows a 26-mile Lt Fl 5s from a W lighthouse on the cliffs 72m above the sea. Its 30M Radio Beacon, callsign "GN" is on 310.3kHz, the same frequency as the 20M beacon at Cap d'Alprech (callsign "PH"). The latter is 2 miles S of Boulogne and has a 24M light Fl (3) 15s from a 15m W tower, B top 62m above sea level. One mile east of the southern jetty head on the shore there is a directional Radio Beacon without callsign on 289.6kHz with a range of only 5 miles. When you are on approach course 101° from seaward it sounds a steady note. If you are N of the beam it sounds letter A; if to the S of track it emits letter N.

The N-going stream starts 2½ hours before HW Dover, turning to the southward 6 hours later. It exceeds 3 knots at springs.

The S-cardinal Boulogne Approach buoy is 2 miles WNW of the entrance with a light VQ (6)+LFl 10s, 7M. At first the entrance may be confusing, because most of the seaward half of the N breakwater is submerged, leaving only a rectangular box structure to carry the small Q R 7M light 10m above the water (pic 3.1). Opinions vary about the amount of water over the sunken breakwater, but most local powerboats and shoal-draft yachts go through the main entrance at all times.

This has a 22m W tower G top showing a Fl (2+1) W lt 15s

3.4 Entrance to Port de Marée, shared by ferries and yacht harbour. Notre Dame cathedral dominates skyline with Casino in foreground. Traffic signals on starboard hand.

with a range of 19 miles. The fog signal is a horn (2 + 1) 60s. Resist the temptation to head straight for the entrance to the ferry port, because shoal water extends 7 cables from the beach on the NE and is uncomfortably close. So head off 2 points to starboard until the inner entrance is fully opened up on the leading lights on 123°.

R and G towers carry FR and FG Lts either side of the entrance. The harbour control tower is on the SW head and exhibits the standard light signals with certain local variations:

G alongside centre Lt: no movements in or out except by ships authorized.

R or $_R^R$ alongside normal Lts: no movements except by ships authorized to depart.

RR: Dredging taking place in main channel (pic 3.5).

34

3.5   *Traffic signals, facing to seaward. The old harbour control structure is on the left, while the dredger is usually there.*

3.6   *Small yacht harbour on west bank.*

3.7   Secondary yacht harbour above Pont Marguet.

These signals are repeated on the E bank facing down-harbour (pic 3.5).

The leading lights are:

Front (on the seaward corner of the Gare Maritime): 3FG on an inverted triangle frame above a W column with R bands.

Rear: FG on a 43m Grey tower R top located on the Quai Gambetta which forms the NE (left) bank of the harbour. It is reserved for fishing boats.

Berthing and Facilities   Alongside the Gare Maritime are two RO/RO ferry terminals in tandem. Immediately upstream of them is the 85-berth Yacht Hbr with a little hut at the inshore end which does duty as the Bureau du Port. Visiting boats should secure to the inshore end of the pontoon parallel to the wall. The clubhouse (tel. (21) 31-80-67) is a mile away, near the casino.

Next there is the Pont Marguet carrying very heavy traffic from downtown Boulogne, which is at its NE end. It has a sluice and a lock-gate under it, which is just as well otherwise the 180 boats on four pontoons in the Arrière-Port would stay there for ever. The lock opens infrequently and only when the tide level in the harbour permits. It is no place for visitors (pic 3.7).

There are plans to expand the Yacht Hbr, but no final decision has been taken (mid 1984).

Although limited in scope, the marina has no depth problems, is well sheltered from any direction and is only a few minutes walk from the centre of town. Weather reports are taped on (21) 31-79-90, or on VHF Ch23 at 0703 and 1733. Area 9 Sandettie.

Communications   The best of any Channel port, with fast trains to Paris (2h), ferries to Dover and Folkestone, flights from near-by Le Touquet.

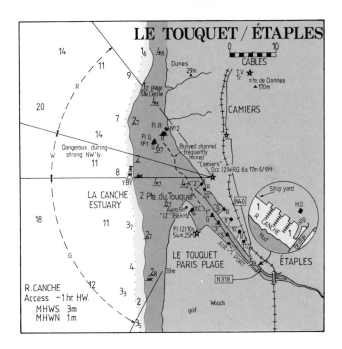

Charts (*BA 2612 ; Fr 3800 ; CG 1011*)
High Water −*ooh 10 Dover* +*ooh 12 SP Dieppe*
Heights above Datum *Springs* *MHW 9m0* *MLW 1m0*
 Neaps *MHW 7m2* *MLW 2m7*

In spite of its full name, Le Touquet-Paris-Plage, it is as much a playground for big-spending Brits as the Parisians who own most of the lovely holiday homes set among the pines and silver birches. It is 175 miles from Paris but only 20 miles from Boulogne and the ferry from England. Those who want to play golf on its two magnificent courses, go to the casino, play tennis, go pony-trekking or take part in the endless leisure events organized by an enterprising local tourist office can also fly into the airport, which features arguably the best restaurant in town.

Not unnaturally yachtsmen who have seen the R. Canche at HW are tempted to think of sailing over the 50 miles from Ramsgate or 65 from the Brighton Marina.

Before doing so, have a look at the accompanying pictures (4.1, 4.2 and 4.3) showing what it is like anywhere near LW. It dries out to a trickle for 2 miles offshore. It is also a horrible entrance to make in strong winds from any direction, particularly so from any W'ly sector. However, 2 miles upstream at Étaples, right off the end of the airport runway, a new yacht marina (1984) has opened, which could tempt the owner of a shoal-draft boat who finds conditions to his liking at the lower part of the estuary.

Generally the river channel will have 3m least depth all the way to Étaples within one hour of HW springs (1m2 at neaps). Entry should not be attempted earlier than 2 hours before HW.

Approach Off the estuary the tide runs northward up to 3¼ knots at springs from 2½h before HW Dover until it turns 3½h after HW Dover.

The most prominent landmark is the 56m Or octagonal lighthouse situated at the northern end of Le Touquet less than 1 mile south of the entrance to the R. Canche. Its Lt is Fl (2) 10s with a range of 25M. Near by is the Air Beacon callsign "LT" on 358kHz. Its range is 20M.

4.1   *The Canche estuary at low water. The bright building on the right bank is at Le Touquet airport.*

On the other bank just $1\frac{1}{2}$ miles N of Le Touquet Lt is the R lattice-work 11m Lt-tower at Camiers. Not so powerful with only 9M range in its W sector is Camiers Lt Oc (2) WRG 6s. Its W sector between 090° and 105° will bring you to the W-cardinal pillar $1\frac{1}{2}$ miles WNW of Pointe du Touquet.

In the R sector (105–141°) and quite close to the N shore will be found the buoys marking the start of the tortuous, shifting, not to say treacherous, channel to the Cercle Nautique du Touquet (CNT). No.1 is a G conical bell buoy with X topmark; its pair, No.2, is a R can whistle buoy with a can topmark.

4.2   *Le Touquet yacht club at low water.*

4.3   *A berth 100 metres off the yacht club. Green buoy and red-topped pillar mark what's left of the channel.*

4.4 The commercial quay at Étaples with work in progress for new yacht pontoons and slips (1984).

From here inward the channel is well marked by G and R buoys usually relocated in time to keep pace with the uncertain meanderings of the channel. Follow a local fishing boat in, with one eye on the echo sounder.

From the YC upstream is straightforward, with the channel clearly marked by R box-topped beacons to port and G triangle-topped beacons to starboard. Just don't cut any corners, as there are sunken training walls on both sides.

Berthing and Facilities A temporary mud berth can be obtained off the CNT where there is a slip and dinghy park (pics 4.2 and 4.3) but, from every point of view, it is better to go on up to Étaples.

On the left bank you first come to the shipyard with its 120-ton lifting capacity for fishing boats and ability to build or repair yachts up to any size which will float on the river.

The town quay immediately upstream from the boatyard gives priority to the local fishing fleet, but yachts may seek permission to secure outboard of them, so long as they are prepared to take the ground.

Between the end of the quay and the bridge carrying the RN39 from Le Touquet to the east there are three sets of new pontoons accommodating 75 boats of under 10m LOA which are prepared to take the ground at LWS if they draw over 1m0. There is also a new hard for launching boats into the river from trailers (pic 4.4).

Enquiries for a berth or for weather forecasts can be made through the YC at Le Touquet (tel. (21) 05-12-77) or by calling the Centre Nautique Canche (CNC) on the waterfront at Étaples (tel. (21) 94–74–26). Area 9 Sandettie.

Customs are at Le Touquet airport.

FW, fuel and shore power are available.

There is the Syndicat d'Initiative on the quayside or, a block farther into the town, the Mairie will be found to be helpful.

Good shops and bistros are available within walking distance.

*5 ST VALÉRY-sur-SOMME/LE CROTOY

Charts   *Fr 3800 ; CG 1011 ; (BA 2612 ; 1m C31)*
High Water   *−00h 00 Dover   +00h 35 SP Dieppe*
Heights above Datum   *Springs   MHW 10m0 MLW 0m7*
      Neaps   MHW 8m0 MLW 2m5

THESE two little villages on either bank near the mouth of the Somme estuary are both worth a visit—but only in settled weather, good visibility, and bearing in mind that the whole estuary dries out to a distance of 4 miles off Pointe le Hourdel, the little fishing village on the S bank nearer the open sea. Le Hourdel rarely has room for visitors and offers few amenities to be worth risking the tricky channel into it.

William the Conqueror embarked at St Valéry for his invasion of England. Joan of Arc was brought there by her English captors from Le Crotoy in 1430. The Somme was the scene of one of the bloodiest battles in the First World War and was no picnic in the Second World War. During the holiday season a narrow-gauge railway links the two little ports through 14km of lovely countryside.

Approach   The critical mark to identify is the N-Cardinal BY buoy 3 miles WNW of Pointe le Hourdel marked 'AT-SO' (short for 'Atterisage–Somme'). Its light is VQ and it lies in the R sector of the 15M light at Ault (Oc (3) 12s). Here the NNE-going current starts 4 hours before HW Dover, turning SSW 2h after HW. The spring rate is 2¾ knots.

Le Hourdel lighthouse is a prominent landmark by day—a W tower G top, 18m high, standing up from a small cluster of houses close to the left-hand edge of the low-lying countryside of dunes and marshes. Its Lt is Oc (3) WG 12s. The AT-SO buoy lies in its W sector, range 12M (pic 5.3).

Some 2½ miles SW of Le Hourdel is another W lighthouse G top Fl R 5s, 22M at an elevation of 32m. It is listed as the Cayeux light, but it is in fact in the village of Brighton.

About 11 miles NNE is the impressive Berck lighthouse at the Pointe du Haut Blanc. On a featureless, flat coastline its 44m tower with four broad R bands on a W background stands out well. The Lt is Fl 5s out to a range of 23M.

Even by the standards of Exmouth or Christchurch, the navigable channel into the Somme is a movable feature, but the G and R channel buoys are repositioned each time the sandbanks move. The total distance to thread one's way to St Valéry is a little over 9 miles, so a good time to depart from AT-SO buoy is 2 hours before HW. When asked for a chart of the channel, the HO at Le Crotoy, which administers both ports, said 'N'existe pas'.

In 1983 the first pair of channel buoys were about ½ mile off the shore almost in line with the Cayeux (Brigthon) lighthouse described above. Thereafter the channel meanders all over the place, but is well marked by sizeable buoys, mostly unlit.

About ½ mile to the E of Pointe le Hourdel there is a RW striped buoy marking the point where the channel splits: *due E* for 1 mile to Le Crotoy along a channel with all its buoys marked 'C'; *to the SE* towards the wooded area on the right bank where the town of St Valéry-sur-Somme lies.

The last 1½ miles of the approach is plainly marked by G beacons to starboard along a mole. At its seaward end there is a Lt Q (3) G 6s on a BW chequered beacon whence the course is 140° for 9 cables. Three of the last seven G beacons carry Fl (2) G 5s lights, including the one where the mole joins the land. The lovely tree-lined embankment leading to the harbour and the entrance of the Somme Canal has a 6m W hut G top at its western end with a 9M light Iso G 4s (pic 5.6).

From here the port hand is marked by a succession of beacons with R can topmarks until reaching the mole parallel to the

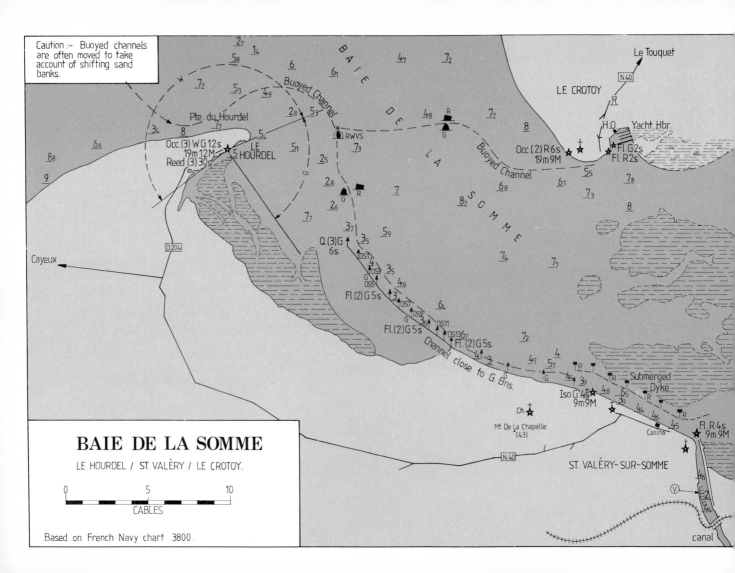

Caution:- Buoyed channels are often moved to take account of shifting sand banks.

2_7 1_4
5_8
6
6_1

B A I E

4_7 7_2

LE CROTOY

Le Touquet

N 40

Pte. du Hourdel

7_2
5_3
4_8

Buoyed Channel

2_8 5_3
3_4

1_7

Occ.(3) WG 12s
19m 12M
Reed (3) 30s

5_4
LE
HOURDEL

5_1

RWVS

2_5

7_3

R
G

4_8

D E

7_2

8

H.Q.   Yacht Hbr.

Occ.(2) R 6s
19m 9M

5_5

6_1

7_8

Fl.G 2s
Fl.R 2s

6_8

8_8
6_6

8

9

7_7

L A

2_8
G   R

7

8_2

7_4

7_3

8

Cayeux

D 204

2_6

3_7

Q.(3) G
6s

3_5
5_9

4_9

3_5

7_7

S O M M E

7_7

DS1

DS3

G
DS5

3_5

3_5

Fl.(2) G 5s

3_5
DS7

6_4

7_2

8

G   DS9
Fl.(2) G 5s

DS11

DS136_1   Fl.(2) G 5s

Channel close to G. Bns.

5_7

4_7 5_7

R

Submerged
Dyke

G

4_4 3_9

R

4_8

Iso G 4s
9m 9M

5_5

Ch.

Mt. De La Chapelle
(43)

4_4 4_6

R

Casino

4_5

Fl.R 4s
9m 9M

N 40

ST. VALÉRY-SUR-SOMME

V

4_6

4_4

canal

BAIE DE LA SOMME

LE HOURDEL / ST. VALÉRY / LE CROTOY.

0   5   10

CABLES

Based on French Navy chart 3800.

5.1 The channel into Le Crotoy with new marina at A.

5.2 The seaward end of the Somme estuary with Le Hourdel in the foreground and St Valéry at B.

quayside which forms the harbour. Its extremity is marked by a W lattice Lt tower Fl R 4s, 9m, 9M.

Berthing The harbour is the last ½ mile of the approach to the 14km canal to Abbeville. To enter it, steer between the tree-lined mole forming its eastern side and the buildings along the quay forming the right bank (pic 5.7).

43

5.3 *Le Hourdel lighthouse.*

5.4 *No room for visitors at Le Hourdel at low water.*

Berths for yachts can be found on pontoons built out from the town quay beyond the coasters and fishing boats (pic 5.8). At the outboard end of the pontoons there is 2m depth at LW. They are perfectly sheltered in all weathers. Of the 290 berths 30 are reserved for visitors.

Facilities The clubhouse of the Sport Nautique Valericain (SNV) is near the marina. Fuel and FW available and there is a 6-ton crane: a boat repair yard is on the dockside. The HO is nearer the harbour entrance on the Quai de Pilotes (tel. (22) 27–52–57), but overall administration is concentrated in Le Crotoy.

St Valéry has a number of hostelries catering mainly for summer visitors, but the locals' own haunts are appetising. There are complete shopping facilities, including an excellent chandlery.

Weather forecasts are posted locally near the Yacht Hbr. Area 9 Sandettie.

LE CROTOY Only $1\frac{1}{2}$ miles N across the Somme estuary is the little fishing village and holiday resort of Le Crotoy (pop. 2,500). Its attractions include a beautiful bathing beach when the tide permits, a modern casino and a famous turn-of-the-century restaurant on the water's edge in which the octogenerian patronne still personally acts as chef.

Approach From the buoy E of Pointe le Hourdel where the fairway splits (see above) follow the R and G buoyed channel towards the 11m high W lattice tower alongside the Casino with its Oc (2) R 6s Lt.

Access can safely be made $1\frac{1}{2}$ hours $\pm$ HW. The channel

5.5   Final approach to St Valéry with channel clearly limited by a mole and training wall.

45

5.6 *Seaward end of the esplanade.*

5.7 *Harbour is entered by leaving tree-lined mole to port.*

5.8 *St Valéry seen looking downstream from Somme Canal locks.*

5.9 Entrance to Le Crotoy marina two hours after low water.

5.10 Harbour wall used by fishermen.

5.11 *Same quay three hours later (an hour before high water).*

swings round the point on which the town is built to enter the little harbour on a N'ly course.

The port-hand jetty at the entrance has a 4m metal R post with a Fl R 2s light. A G post on the other breakwater has a light Fl G 2s (pic 5.10).

Berthing and Facilities   The harbour has been dredged to a least depth of 1m at the new pontoons, so it may be necessary to take the mud in a keelboat and time one's visit before springs to avoid being neaped. Fishing boats secure alongside the western quay, where a visiting yacht could secure long enough to contact the local HO, which is a block farther into the town (tel. (22) 27–81–44).

The near-by Club Nautique de la Baie de Somme (CNBS) keeps the pontoons mostly for its members. In all there are shoal-draft berths for 280 boats. Visitors will be allocated berths on the S side of the pontoons. The CNBS normally only functions in July and August, but has basic facilities.

Facilities ashore are in character with any small fishing port.

PART THREE

NORMANDY

Le Tréport—Cherbourg

Soundings and heights in metres
Bearings and courses in degrees true
Distances at sea in nautical miles or cables

NORMANDIE, CALVADOS, CONTENTIN

Safe navigable distances from breakwater to breakwater (in nautical miles)

	LE TRÉPORT	DIEPPE	ST VALÉRY-EN-CAUX	FÉCAMP	LE HAVRE	HONFLEUR	DEAUVILLE/TROUVILLE	OUISTREHAM	COURSEULLES	PORT-EN-BESSIN	ST VAAST	CHERBOURG (W)
LE TRÉPORT												
DIEPPE	13											
ST VALÉRY-EN-CAUX	28	15										
FÉCAMP	43	30	15									
LE HAVRE	66	53	38	23								
HONFLEUR	74	61	45	30	11							
DEAUVILLE/TROUVILLE	72	59	44	29	6	9						
OUISTREHAM	81	68	53	37	18	21	14					
COURSEULLES	83	75	55	40	23	28	21	11				
PORT-EN-BESSIN	92	80	64	49	34	40	33	23	12			
ST VAAST	104	95	78	63	53	59	53	46	35	24		
CHERBOURG (W)	118	108	82	77	70	77	72	58	54	45	26	

*6 LE TRÉPORT

Charts   *BA 1351 ; Fr 5928 ; CG 1011 ; Im C31*
High Water   *—00h 30 Dover   —01h 10 SP Dunkerque*
Heights above Datum   *Springs   MHW 9m4   MLW 0m7*
Neaps   MHW 7m4   MLW 2m4

A SMALL fishing port at the mouth of the R. Bresle about half-way between Dieppe and the Somme estuary at Pointe de Hourdel. Local industry is supplied by coastal vessels drawing up to 15ft, in spite of the outer harbour's drying out to over a cable to seaward of the breakwaters. The shingly beach on the eastern side of the town (Mers-les-Bains) is for some reason popular with holidaymakers camping in the district. But the whole scene is discouraging to visiting yachtsmen, especially as they are obliged to berth nearly ½ mile away from the civilized part of the town. The aerial picture (6.1) 2h after LW, taken during August, shows how few yachts have gone through the lock to their assigned berths top right of the Bassin à Flot. The remainder are on mud berths either side of the channel leading to the lock.

About 4km inland, perhaps the best reason for a yachtsman to visit Le Tréport, is the ancient town of Eu, with its twelfth-century abbey curiously dedicated jointly to Notre Dame and St Laurent O'Toole, primate of Ireland.

Approach   From a distance Le Tréport appears as a break in the cliffs, like so many other small ports on this coast. On wooded high ground inland of the port is a prominent water tower, while the square tower of the church of St Jacques in the middle of the town is equally prominent. The eastern side is dominated by factory buildings.

At night the W sector of the 19M Lt at Ault—3½ miles NE

6.1   *Few yachts in the Bassin à Flot (A). Lock-gates shut (B). Mud berths on port hand assigned to local yacht club (C).*

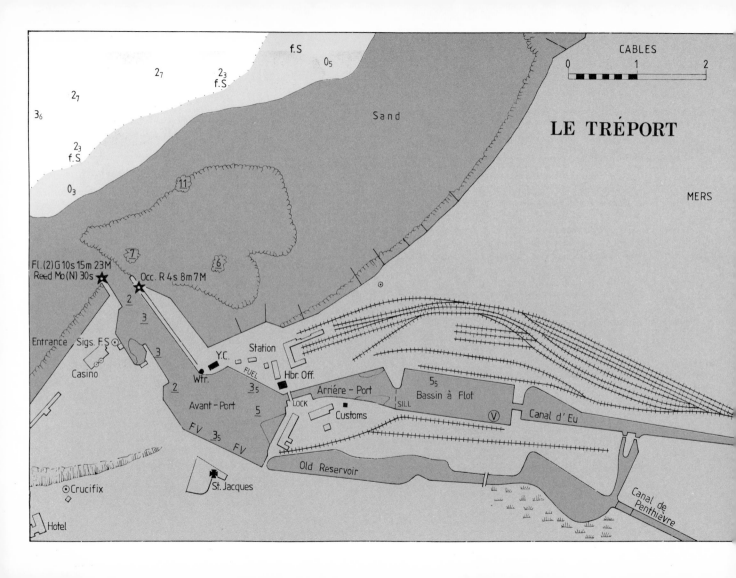

6.2   Modest yacht club on the east side, facing to seaward.

of Le Tréport (Oc (3) WR 12s, 95m high)—may be picked up
together with the 20M light at the end of the W breakwater at
the harbour entrance (Fl (2) G 10s, 15m high). It is a W tower
G top. It sounds a reed every 30s in fog—morse "N".

Approaching on a SE'ly course, the E jetty Lt is on a 7m W
column with a R top and base. Its Lt is Oc R 4s. Beside it stand
the light signals controlling harbour traffic (pic 6.1), using the
Simplified Code.

The tidal stream runs across your approach course up to 2
knots at springs.

Two miles E of the town at Eu airfield there is a 20M Aerobeacon on 330kHz callsign "EU".

Arrival should be timed to coincide with the opening of the

lock into the Bassin à Flot, which is 1½h before HW.

In NW'ly winds entry is not recommended. The Avant-Port
is not at all comfortable and no place to hang about.

Berthing   Once inside the Avant-Port it may be possible in
settled weather to secure alongside the Quai Francois Ier on the
SW side in the heart of the town, although it is usually reserved
for fishing boats. The Quai Bellot on the opposite side is shared
by the pilot boat and club moorings assigned by the YCB (Yacht
Club de Bresle), a modest building at the inshore end of the E
jetty (pic 6.2).

When the lock-gate is open, if need be sound three blasts to
get the bridge open as well. Then proceed straight through the
Arrière-Port to the Bassin à Flot. Yachts may not berth in the

6.3   *Club moorings seen from clubhouse toward locks.*

6.4   *View to seaward from lock-gates at half-tide.*

former. Some charts still show a lock between these two basins, but it has been demolished (pic 6.1).

Facilities   FW can be obtained on the dockside. Fuel is just outside the lock-gate, right by the Bureau du Port (tel. (35) 86–17–91) on the E side.

There is a fully-equipped boatyard immediately through the second lock, the seaward end of the Eu Canal.

There is a casino facing the western beach with the local Office of Tourism in it. Adequate shopping and bistros.

*7 DIEPPE

Charts *BA 2147 ; Im C31 ; Fr 5927 ; (Fr 934 ; CG 1012 ; Stan 1)*
High Water *—00h 30 Dover —01h 10 SP Dunkerque*
Heights above Datum *Springs* MHW 9m3 MLW 0m7
                          Neaps MHW 7m2 MLW 2m5

DIEPPE is a greatly underrated town and resort. Our grandfathers swore by it—indeed many of them lived there, alongside Aubrey Beardsley, Sickert, Whistler and Oscar Wilde, to write, paint or keep a low profile towards their creditors. It has all the facilities Deauville has to offer, except polo and the jet-setters. The casino, gourmet restaurants and high quality hotels abound in the old town facing the beach. Day-trippers from Newhaven, 65 miles away, swarm to the hypermarket on the edge of town or blow their money in the open markets just a block away from the ferry landing. The surrounding countryside is not unlike Devon.

The beach is advertised as being the nearest to Paris (200km or 2h by train). It is also a memorial to the famous Anglo-Canadian Raid in August 1942. The fact that the raiding forces were denied a covering barrage or a softening-up air bombardment preserved all the old buildings, at the expense of filling the war graves' plot on the road to the airport. As the official guide still says : '. . . their sacrifice hastened the day when the Nazi yoke was lifted from France'.

In days gone by it was the centre of the ivory trade. Until container ships took over a decade ago it was the principal port for bringing in bananas and other exotic vegetables. Now its principal trade is provided by the RO/RO ferries from Newhaven.

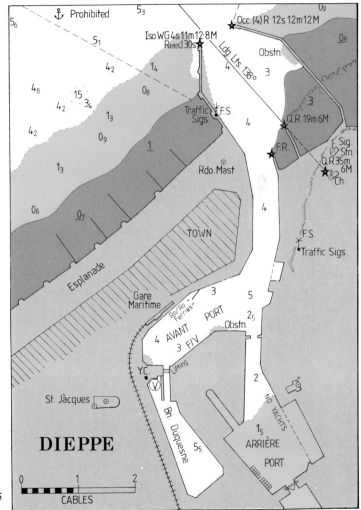

7.1 *Bassin Duquesne is top right (A) accessible through swing-bridge from ferry terminal (B). Note only fishing boats are on the waiting berths (C).*

7.2 *Seaward end of west breakwater. (Photo : Debbie Godfray)*

7.3 *Eastern mole. Note the channel flood making across the entrance.*

Unfortunately, of all the ways to get to Dieppe and enjoy its charms, going by yacht is not the easiest or necessarily the most pleasant. The harbour entrance funnels in a nasty swell when it blows from the NW. The outer harbour has a pontoon designated for yachts waiting to lock into the old Port de Pêche, now the Bassin Duquesne. But more than likely a local fishing boat will get there first. If you lie outboard there is a fair chance of being crunched by the ferry turning through 180° to sail with

7.4 *Semaphore station and Notre Dame de Bon-Secours on the eastern skyline, with traffic signals on the west side.*

7.5 *Lifting bridge from Avant-Port to yacht harbour with the old Seajet terminal on the right.*

7.6   Berths in the Bassin Duquesne seen on entry.

7.7   The yacht club—Cercle de la Voile de Dieppe (CVD)—is the white, hutted building to the left of the lifting bridge. However, it is in the heart of town.

only feet to spare—or at least being scared out of your wits. To cap that, the Avant-Port is filthy dirty, with oil, flotsam and garbage piled into it by each nor'wester. However, many think these preliminaries are well worth surmounting.

Approach   The town is just 4 miles E of the imposing Pointe d'Ailly with its W square tower G top lighthouse 24m high, 98m above sea level. The Lt is Fl (3) 20s to a range of 34M. There is a reed (3) 60s in fog. On top of that it has a Radio Beacon on 310.3kHz, callsign "A" in the same group as the Royal Sovereign and also 50M range.

The town lies in a widish gap between white cliffs about 30m high. There is no less than 3m5 water all the way into the Avant-Port so, subject to the problem spelled out above, you can go in on any state of the tide. The belfry of Notre Dame de Bon-Secours on the skyline to the east of the town is conspicuous by day on making the correct approach course of 138°. The W signal station alongside the church is also prominent.

Make for the breakwater heads, allowing for a tide which can run up to 2 knots across the entrance, starting to the E at −05h 30 Dover, turning W at HW Dover. The W jetty head has a 7m W tower G top (Lt Iso WG 4s 12/8M). The W sector is about 3 points either side of the correct lead in.

The E jetty head has a W tower R top 8m high with a Lt Oc (4) R 12s.

The transit Lts are:

Front: on the old E jetty, a W metal frame R top 16m high Q R.

Rear: on clifftop 35m up a W hut R top and another Q R Lt.

At this point it is imperative to obey the local traffic signals. They are put out on VHF Ch12. They are also displayed visually on the W jetty and at the corner of the harbour where one rounds up to get into Avant-Port. The full code is used (RWR = don't enter. GWG = don't sail. GWR = don't move).

There are additional signals used at the same time: for cross-channel ferries entering, by day Flag N (Bu and W chequers); at night, a G light; a ferry departing is notified by day by pendant 4 (W St George's Cross on R pendant), at night by a R light. The ferries always have priority.

Assuming one has timed one's arrival to go straight into the Bassin Duquesne (−2h to +1h on HW) the flag P will be flown to indicate that the lock is open. Two long blasts on the foghorn might activate the bridge operator (pic 7.5).

Berthing and Facilities Immediately inside the lock there is a pontoon and some alongside berths on the western quayside. Unfortunately there are only 80 berths available (1983). The YC (Cercle de Voile de Dieppe—CVD) has a modest clubhouse just by the lock (tel. (35) 84–32–99). FW, fuel and some repair facilities are available on the spot. The shopping and eating out have no parallel—all within a few minutes' walk of the boat.

Weather forecaste on VHF Ch2 at 0633 and 1133. They are also displayed at the clubhouse or can be obtained from Rouen by tel. (35) 80–11–44. Area 10 Manche est. Duty-free stores are available. Customs are on the Descroisilles (tel. (35) 84–24–47).

*8 ST VALÉRY-EN-CAUX

Charts *CG 1012 (Fr 6794 ; Im C31 ; BA 2612)*
High Water *—00h 45 Dover —01h 25 SP Dunkerque*
Heights above Datum *Springs MHW 8m9 MLW 0m9*
Neaps MHW 7m1 MLW 2m4

St Valéry is built around a natural harbour situated in a valley between the white cliffs stretching from Dieppe to Fécamp. It is exactly half-way between the two. A former fishing port, it is now given over almost entirely to those using the 550-boat Yacht Hbr or the beach. Overlooking the harbour from the cliffs d'Amont is the memorial to the men of the 51st Highland Division who fought their last battle here in 1940 before the Panzers wiped them out and most of the town with them.

Approach Since the Avant-Port dries out a cable to seaward of the breakwaters forming the entrance, no attempt should be made to enter before half-tide. There are drying-out berths alongside the quays and a few moorings on which to wait, but it is best to reach the lock when it opens ±2h HW for boats drawing 1m50.

Approach the harbour entrance on a SSE'ly course. The more prominent lighthouse is on the western breakwater, which protrudes farther to seaward. Its Lt is on a G tower and shows Oc (2+1) G 12s, 13m, 13M. At the seaward end of the eastern arm is a W frame tower R top and a Lt Fl (2) R 6s, 9m, 5M. Favour the E side of the fairway to the Avant-Port. The worst conditions for entering are in a NNE'ly wind.

Across the locks is a lifting bridge, which opens on the hour and half-hour whenever the lock-gates are open (pics 8.3 and 8.4).

Berthing Visitors should make for the pontoons immediately inside the locks on the starboard hand (Quai du Havre).

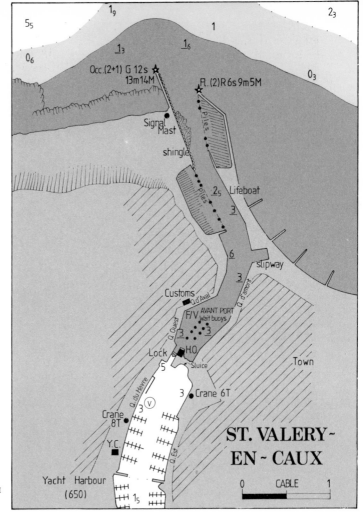

8.1   This half-tide shot shows how the entrance channel shoals on the west side.

8.2   Perches marking the entrance channel. Note the swell running in on the starboard hand in light weather.

8.3   Right ahead are the sluice gates.

8.4   Lifting bridge at the lock-gates.

8.5   The Port de Plaisance. Note how the fairway is marked by heavy piles anchoring the pontoons from each bank.

The HO is on the E side of the bridge over the lock (tel. (35) 97–01–30). The water inside is maintained at 5m over datum. The aerial picture (8.1) shows that there are the supports of an old bridge beyond the fifth pontoon. The channel through them is clearly marked.

Facilities   There are two YCs of interest to visiting yachtsmen, both located on the western side of the inner harbour. The Club Nautique Valeriquais (CNV) is the newer of the two, the other being the Centre de Voile de St Valéry-en-Caux (CVSV). Their telephone numbers are: CNV (35) 97–10–88, CVSV (35) 97–04–22. There is no harbour VHF voice channel.

FW, fuel, repairs and chandlery are all readily available, as are the usual facilities of a holiday port.

Weather forecasts posted at the Bureau du Port and at both YCs. Area 10 Manche est.

*9 FÉCAMP

Charts *BA 1351 ; FR 932 ; 1m C31 ; (CG 1012 ; Stan 1)*
High Water *— 01h 00 Dover — 01h 35 SP Dunkerque*
Heights above Datum *Springs MHW 7m9 MLW 0m8*
Neaps MHW 6m5 MLW 2m5

FÉCAMP lies 10 miles ENE of Cap d'Antifer (Fl 20s 128m, 30M) and 28 miles WSW of Dieppe. It is readily identifiable from seaward because the white cliffs rise steeply to the E from the harbour entrance to an elevation of 120m. The square tower of Notre Dame du Salut dominates the skyline above Pointe Fagnet, with a W signal tower and TV mast near by.

The town has known better days as the main homeport for a fleet of deep-sea trawlers bringing back cod from as far afield as Greenland and the White Sea. It is still the base for a substantial fleet of coastal fishing boats and some commercial traffic in timber, liquid gas and minerals.

Approach Apart from the rocks extending 1½ cables to seaward from Pointe Fagnet there are no off-lying dangers. A boat drawing 1m50 can enter at any state of the tide, but a nasty swell runs through the narrow entrance when the wind is from the W–N sector. In such weather it is best not to enter until an hour before HW.

On rising ground to the SW there is a prominent water tower. Just to the left are the church towers of St Etienne and La Trinité. All three features are clearly shown in the aerial picture 9.1.

The entrance, which is only 200ft wide, lies between the N breakwater with its Grey tower R top (Fl (2) 10s, 15m, 16M) and the G tower (QG 14m, 5M) at the end of the S breakwater. The main Lt sounds a reed (2) 30s in bad visibility.

There is also a Q R at the inshore end of the N breakwater.

9.1 Note the line of moorings in the Arrière-Port (A), but visitors are encouraged to go to the pontoons by the yacht club (B). Berths in the Bassin Berigny (C) are quieter.

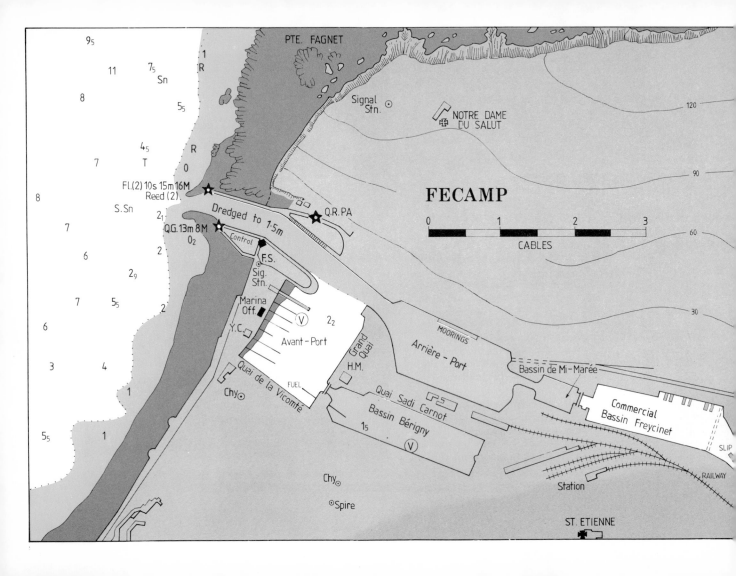

PTE. FAGNET

Signal
Stn. ⊙

⌗ NOTRE DAME
✝ DU SALUT

120

9₅

11   7₅
        Sn

8   5₅

4₅
7   R
        T   0

8

S. Sn

7   2₁

Fl.(2) 10s 15m 16M
Reed (2)

QG.13m 8M   0₂

6   2

2₉

7   5₅   2

6

3   4   1

5₅   1

FECAMP

0   1   2   3

CABLES

Q.R. PA

Dredged to 1·5m

Control

F.S.
Sig.
Stn.

Marina
Off. ■

Y.C. □

Avant – Port

FUEL

Quai de la Vicomté

Chy ⊙

V   2₂

Grand Quai

H.M.

Quai Sadi Carnot

Bassin Bérigny

1₅

V

Arrière – Port

MOORINGS

Bassin de Mi-Marée

Commercial
Bassin Freycinet

SLIP

RAILWAY

Station

Chy ⊙

⊙ Spire

ST. ETIENNE

90

60

30

9.2   A nasty swell runs through the entrance. Minutes later this boat was under full sail and perfectly happy.

9.3   Société des Régates de Fécamp (SRF) clubhouse and Bureau du Port.

9.4   *Boats on the pontoon immediately outside locks, with the fuelling jetty just off the frame to the right.*

9.5   *A boat emerging from the Bassin Berigny.*

9.6   Ten miles WSW along the coast to the impressive Cap d'Antifer lighthouse.

Controls   There is a signal mast above a small office at the inshore end of the S breakwater, which controls traffic using the Simplified Code (see p. 15). A R flat of Lt indicates 'no entry'; G indicates departures forbidden, while R over G orders no movement in or out of the harbour.

The same mast flies code flag P (the Blue Peter) when the lock-gates are open, usually −1½ on HW until 30min afterwards. VHF watch is kept on Ch16.

Berthing   It is possible to go straight ahead through the Passe Botton into the Arrière-Port (pic 9.1) and pick up a mooring off the Quay Guy de Maupassant (he lived there), but there are eight runs of pontoons in the Avant-Port forming a 250-berth marina with all mod-cons. Visiting yachts should berth on the third or fourth pontoon after rounding to starboard to enter the marina area.

The berthing office is situated in the YC house: Societé des Régates de Fécamp (SRF), tel. (35) 28–08–44.

For a more peaceful berth away from the scend, which rarely dies down, go through the lock to the Bassin Bérigny—upper right, pic 9.1. The Bureau du Port is just N (left) of the lock-gate. Here the depth is maintained at 5m. Outside in the Avant-Port it is shown as 1m50, but a visit in 1984 revealed that 2m is now claimed for most of the berths.

Facilities   FW on the pontoons. Fuel just to the right of the lock leading to Bassin Bérigny. The latter is for commerical traffic, but has a comprehensive boatyard there (Ch. C. Moré tel. (35) 28–28–15).

There is a slipway in the NW corner of the Avant-Port. Good restaurants and all provisioning needs can be met.

Weather reports posted at the YC or on tape from Le Havre on tel. (35) 42–12–19. Area 10 Manche est.

SNCF to Le Havre, Rouen and Paris.

Customs tel. (35) 28–19–40.

10 LE HAVRE

Charts	*BA 2146 ; Fr 6683 ; Im 31 ; CG 1012 ; (Stan 1)*		
	Carte Guide de Navigation Fluviale : 'Paris à la mer		
	par le canal de Tancarville'		
High Water	*−01h 18 Dover SP Le Havre*		
Heights above Datum	*Springs*	*MHW 7m8*	*MLW 1m1*
	Neaps	*MHW 6m5*	*MLW 2m8*

LE HAVRE is a busy commercial centre of 250,000 inhabitants, almost completely rebuilt since 1945. It has successfully made the transition from being an international passenger terminal for great liners to being the third largest cargo port in Europe (con-tainer ships and tankers). It is also a popular RO/RO ferry terminal for traffic to Southampton or Portsmouth.

For yachtsmen it is mainly of interest because its deep-water channels are unaffected by the state of the tide, there is a modern marina and it gives access to the placid waters of the Tancarville Canal 25km along the 115km to Rouen or 360km to Paris, thus avoiding the somewhat exposed estuary seas in the lower reaches of the Seine.

Approach   If coming from the Solent or farther west, touch-down should be near the Le Havre buoy (replacing the old LV), which is fully described in the chapter on Deauville. From this point it is 10½ miles down a well-buoyed channel. Twin chimneys each 247m high are close to the leading line (pic 10.2), while the tower of St Joseph's church (105m) near the YC is also promi-nent, on the port bow.

10.1   Cap de la Hève lighthouse stands out better from sea level. Note prominent communications pylon with dish antenna just to its right.

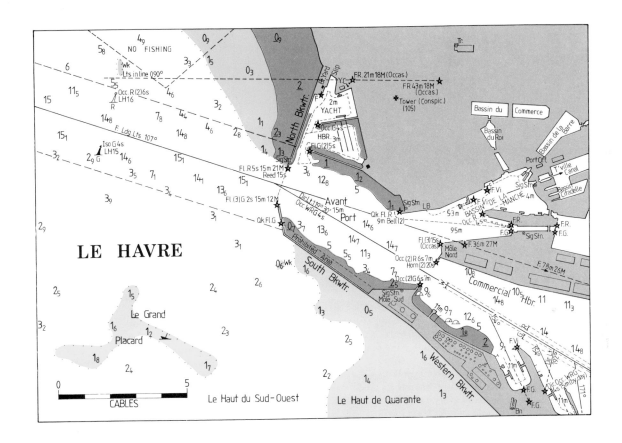

LE HAVRE

Le Grand
Placard

Le Haut du Sud-Ouest

Le Haut de Quarante

0   CABLES   5

10.2 *The twin 247-metre chimneys can be seen for miles and are close to the leading line on the main fairway. The yacht harbour is to the left of the north breakwater entrance.*

Although the two leading Lts are on tall Grey towers (35m and 77m) they cannot be picked out by day. At night 27-mile fixed W Lts are intensified 1 degree either side of the 107° leading line.

Boats approaching from the NE can round the prominent Cap de la Hève close to and shape straight for the harbour entrance 2 miles distant. The lighthouse is a W octagonal tower 32m high with a R top, standing at 123m elevation above the sea. Its Lt is Fl W 5s with a range of 24M (pic 10.1).

The breakwaters at the entrance each have 15m W tower structures at their ends. The northernmost one has a R top and a 21-mile Fl R 5s Lt. It also sounds a reed every 15s in poor visibility. The S one has a G top; its 12-mile Lt is VQ (3) G 2s.

Give the end of the N breakwater a wide berth and swing to port to a NNE'ly course parallel to the N breakwater. The

entrance to the Yacht Hbr is between it and the end of the Digue Augustin Normand, which protects the berths from S–SW'ly blows. At its western extremity it has a weak Q (2) G 5s Lt on a G metal pole. There is an inner mole also with a Lt at its W end (Oc G 4s).

Berthing The Anse de Joinville (least depth 3m0) between the two inner moles described above has 40 berths on the first of its pontoons for visitors. The other 600 berths are either on the other two pontoons or on moorings in Port des Yachts south of the imposing YC building, Société des Régates du Havre (SRH). Close to the NE corner of the inner harbour there is less water, down to 1m1.

VHF traffic on Ch12, 16, 20 and 22 are for controlling commercial shipping. Yachts should contact the HM on tel. (35) 21–23–93 or the HO on (35) 22–81–40.

10.3 St Joseph's Church. A prominent landmark near the yacht club.

10.4 Harbour entrance seen from the yacht club. Note that there are no pontoons in the inner harbour—only booms and buoys.

For longer stays and only by pre-arrangement it is possible to move up-harbour and through three locks to the Bassin du Commerce.

Facilities FW and fuel can all be obtained in the Yacht Hbr. Near the YC there is a slipway and a boatyard with cranes. Also a chandler who is a main agent for French Navy charts and carries a selection of British ones.

The Société des Régates du Havre (SRH tel. (35) 42-41-21) is prestigious, well appointed, active in promoting international racing and has the best restaurant of any yacht club in the north of France (pic 10.5). It is open and well supported all the year round. Visiting yachtsmen who conform to local standards and don't stroll in wearing tee-shirts and frayed denim pants are welcome. It's worth the effort, since there are few other places to eat or drink within walking distance of the Yacht Hbr. Le Havre's city centre is of little interest.

The Customs are at 201 Boulevard de Strasbourg, a taxi-ride up-town (tel. (35) 42–79–26).

Weather forecasts can be obtained on (35) 21–16–11 or on VHF Ch82 at 0633 and 1133. Area 10 Manche est.

10.5   Société de Régates du Havre—'best food in any yacht club in Northern France', but don't arrive in a tee-shirt and frayed pants. The white building to the right is a main chart supplier and chandler.

To Rouen via the Tancarville Canal

Access to the Canal involves going through five locks, starting with that leading into the Bassin de la Citadelle (see plan) which is 1 mile up-harbour at the far end of the Bassin de la Manche (Arrière-Port). Charts BA 2990 and 2994 or Fr 6796 should then be consulted or, even better, the French guide from the sea to Paris quoted at the head of this chapter. Its text is in French, English and German. CG 1012 is perfectly adequate as far as Rouen.

*11 HONFLEUR

Charts *(BA 2146 ; Fr 6796 ; CG 1012 (Approach only))*
High Water *—01h 35 Dover —00h 25 SP Le Havre*
Heights above Datum *Springs MHW 7m9 MLW 1m3*
Neaps MHW 6m6 MLW 2m7

HONFLEUR is a mediaeval port of refuge lying off the S bank of the Seine estuary, 7 miles up the deep-water channel towards Rouen and beyond. The old Bassin de l'Ouest in the heart of the city—now the Yacht Hbr—is surrounded by reminders of Honfleur's glorious years. Cartier and Champlain both sailed west from here, the latter founding Quebec in 1608.

Right alongside the lock into the Yacht Hbr is the seat of the Governor in the sixteenth century, known as La Lieutenance, since he was the king's lieutenant. Today it houses the HO.

Also near by is the sixteenth-century Church of St Catherine, uniquely built entirely of wood. In the higher parts of the town, especially by the crucifix of Notre Dame de Grâce, there are wonderful views of the whole Seine estuary.

Approach Approximately 2½ miles SW of the main entrance to Le Havre is the Rade de la Carosse where the Chenal de Rouen starts at the Priesland R buoy (No. 4) Oc (2) R. It lies in the W sector of the Falaise des Fonds Lt, a W square tower with a G top 15m high, situated ¾ mile W of the entrance to Honfleur. It is Fl (3) WRG 12s and has a range of 18M in the W sector. The G sector warns of the extensive Banc du Ratier.

The channel itself is clearly marked by pairs of R and G buoys all the way to G buoy No. 19, right on the doorstep of Honfleur. This is dominated by the W 37m-high Traffic Control Tower with a prominent observation platform at its top immediately under the radars controlling steamer traffic.

11.1   *Taken at one hour before high water, so traffic is all moving inward. At low water it dries almost to the entrance. The yacht harbour is at (A) in the picture.*

76

11.2   The prominent control tower at the entrance directing traffic along the Seine estuary.

11.3   Signal tower and lighthouse controlling entrance to Bassin de l'Est.

11.4   Lock-gates to Bassin de l'Est. Not for yachts.

11.5 *The old building (centre) is La Lieutenance where the Harbour Office is located. Sometimes visitors arriving by night secure alongside the small cut to the right, waiting for the lock-gates to open. But they are to the left.*

The entrance is marked on its western head by a G frame tower 10m high with Q G Lt. On the other side, by the control tower, is a similar Y tower, QW Lt. In low visibility its reed sounds (5) 40s.

At LW the approach dries almost out to the entrance, so it is as well to time one's arrival to about HW $-\frac{1}{2}$h. If early, one can get out of the fierce tidal current sweeping past the entrance at 5 knots or more by ducking inside the entrance and waiting

there in mid channel. The flood runs only $4\frac{1}{2}$h, after which there is a 2h stand.

There are three basins accessible through locks, but only the Bassin de l'Ouest is suitable for visiting yachts.

Protruding into the middle of the main fairway is a point joined to the eastern shore by a sluice-gate. It has a tall signal mast with an enormous crossyard from which are displayed the shapes and lights to control traffic and indicate depths for ships going into

11.6   Lifting bridge and lock-gates to Bassin de l'Ouest.

the commercial harbours (Bassin de l'Est). Alongside it is a prominent W lighthouse with a R top 12m high with a Lt Oc (2) R 6s (pic 11.3).

At this point you should sound one blast to denote your intention of entering the yacht harbour. You can also call on VHF Ch11 or 16.

Swinging to starboard you enter the Avant-Port, the bridge and lock-gate are both on the left of the prominent building La Lieutenance. The lock-gates carry the main road and only open intermittently during suitable tides at times displayed outside La Lieutenance. Fishing boats may be lying in the small cut on your starboard bow and alongside the town quay to port. You can secure briefly to the jetty on the NW side of the bridge, but it is not recommended to take the ground there.

Berthing The Yacht Hbr has pontoon walkways round three sides of it. Secure bows to the pontoon and for choice pick up two stern buoys. There are some alongside berths immediately to port of the lock entrance and there is a slip by the HO. The depth is 2m8.

Yachts with their crews on board may stop for only a week.

11.7 *Boats berth bows-on to pontoons all round the yacht harbour secured astern to small mooring-buoys. Well worth the effort of getting there.*

Facilities Honfleur caters more for tourists and artists than yachtsmen. Nevertheless there is an excellent yacht yard on the eastern jetty and mechanics are available. The old town has great charm; there are plenty of shops, restaurants, banks and hotels. The harbour is completely sheltered from all weathers. But there is no near by yacht club with marina facilities and diesel fuel has to be carried from a local garage.

The HO is on tel. (31) 89–20–02. The lock-keeper tel. (31) 89–22–57. The Customs are on tel. (31) 89–12–13. Traffic control is on VHF Ch11 or 16.

Weather forecasts can be obtained by telephone to (31) 88–28–62. Area 10 Manche est.

There is an SNCF railway station and bus services to Le Havre (1h) or Deauville ($\frac{3}{4}$h).

Charts *BA 1349 ; Fr 6928 ; Im C 32 ; (BA 2146 ; Stan 1)*
High Water *—01h 30 Dover —00h 55 Springs SP Le Havre*
—00h 10 Neaps SP Le Havre
Heights above Datum *Springs MHW 7m7 MLW 1m1*
Neaps MHW 6m5 MLW 2m8

THE TWIN towns of Deauville and Trouville are separated by the R. Touques which all but dries on most tides. To the E the Trouville bank alongside the tree-lined Boulevard F. Moureaux is reserved for fishermen as far upstream as the bridge joining the two towns. It is one long open-air fishmarket, with a wide choice of restaurants and shops on the other side of the road. Dominating the river entrance and the most conspicuous feature from seaward is the baroque casino with its thalassatherapy and cult movies.

To the W lies one of the favourite watering holes of the jet set—Deauville. If as a break from cruising you fancy a round of golf, a chukka of polo or losing your shirt among the Beautiful People either at the race track or on the tables, it's all here during August. You can 'walk the planks' along the edge of the beach and wave in fantasy to the whole cast, from Scott Fitzgerald to the Aly Khan, sipping Dom Perignon outside Ciro's modest little beach café. Today it's as likely to be Tory landowners, entrepreneurs accoutred by Gucci or dishevelled pop stars with their elegant doxies.

The Trouville scene is not so glittering as Deauville, but it shows more life off-season and is generally less expensive.

There are only two choices open to visiting yachtsmen: the new marina (Port Deauville) inside a breakwater built out from the beach, or the two adjoining yacht basins of earlier vintage on the western side of the river. The inner one (Bassin Morny) is the home of the Deauville YC, where visiting British yachtsmen have been welcomed for generations.

Approach Arrival should be planned so as not to reach the entrance before half-tide. If there is a strong onshore wind and sea it is prudent to allow an extra hour's tide. In normal weather it is perfectly safe to enter by night. The point to make for is the unlit Trouville SW W-cardinal bell buoy (YBY) about 1 mile WNW of the harbour entrance.

On passage from the South Coast Leave the Le Havre outer fairway buoy to port, the buoy is R with a Radio Beacon callsign "LH" on 291.9kHz, range 30 miles. The light is Fl(2) R 10s, 10m, 10M. At this point it is 13 miles to the Trouville buoy, so the beacon can be useful as a back bearing.

Leave to starboard the Northgate N-cardinal buoy, Q Lt 3 miles to the WSW of the Le Havre buoy and, at a distance of 4 miles to the SW the three cardinal buoys surrounding the 12m high platform marking the Banc de Seine. Its Lt is 2 Mo U 15s, 10M. The foghorn 30s also uses the morse "U" (· · —).

A course made good of 130° will cut through the R sector of the 7M Dives light (Oc (2 + 1) 12s) until picking up the W sector of the Trouville W breakwater (Fl 4s—B pylon on dolphin 16m high) at a range of 12M. The G sector says you're getting too far to the E. The W sector of the E breakwater Lt (Fl (4) WR 12s W metal tower R top 15m high) just open of the W jetty light will bring you on to the two leading lights located near the right-hand edge of the casino on Pointe de la Cahotte. Both the breakwaters are submerged at HW, but are marked by beacons. The leading lights in transit on 150° are as follows:
Front—Oc R 4s 12M on a W tower with R top 11m high.
Rear—Oc R 4s 10M on a W metal tower R top 17m high.
If approaching from the N or E (eg Le Havre or Honfleur) it

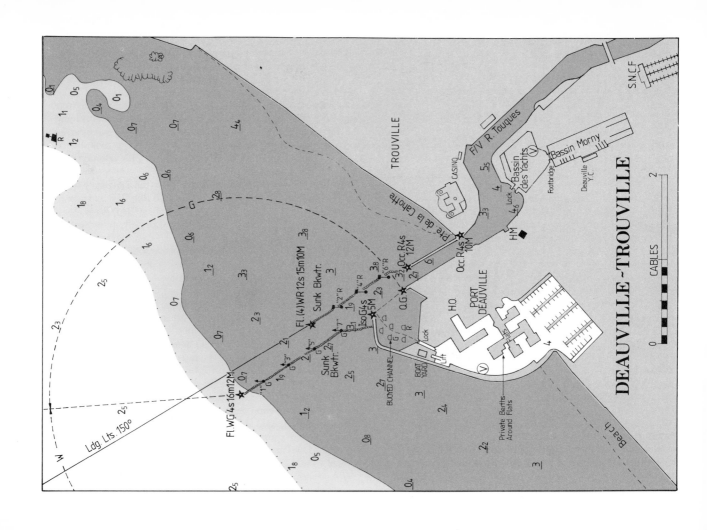

DEAUVILLE-TROUVILLE

TROUVILLE

S.N.C.F

F/V R. Touques

Bassin Morny

Bassin des Yachts

Footbridge

Deauville Y.C.

CASINO

Pte. de la Cahotte

5₅

4

3₃

Lock

4₆

Occ.R4s 10M

HM

Occ.R4s 12M

6

"6"R

3₈

2₃

3₈

"4"R

Q.G.

G R

H.O.

PORT DEAUVILLE

Lock

G R

BLOKED CHANNEL

Lift

BOAT YARD

Private Berths Around Flats

Beach

Sunk Bkwtr.
3

Fl.(4)WR12s 15m10M

3₈

0₆

1₂

3₃

0₆

0₇

2₃

2₁

0₇

3₂

2₇

0₇

1₂

2₃

0₈

2₄

3

2₄

2₂

0₄

0₅

1₈

2₅

"7"

"2"R

1₉

"5"

IsoG4s 5M

3

2₅

3

Sunk Bkwtr.
2₇

"3"

"1"

1₉

2

"1"

0₇

Fl.WG4s16m12M

1₂

0₇

2₁

G

2₈

1₆

0₆

0₆

4₄

0₇

0₇

0₁

0₅

0₁

0₄

0₁

1₁

R

1₂

1₈

1₆

1₆

2₅

2₃

W

Ldg. Lts. 150°

2₅

2₅

CABLES

0   1   2

12.1   Near the top of the tide. Right fore is Port Deauville. The lock-gates into the old yacht harbour (A) are open and even the fishing vessels berthed along the left bank of the River Touques (B) are afloat.

is essential to keep clear of the shoal water—Banc du Ratier and Les Ratelets—which extend 7 miles due W of Honfleur and discourage any corner-cutting. The E cardinal Semoy buoy (BYB) Q (3) 15s lies two miles NNW of Trouville and is within 3° of the leading transit described above. Leave it close to starboard as it marks wrecks close to seaward.

Waiting for the tide, it is recommended to anchor about 5 cables to seaward of the Trouville SW buoy: W-cardinal

12.2 *Looking to seaward at near low water, the west breakwater extension is nearly awash with the beacons all to be left to starboard before turning sharply into the channel for Port Deauville, or carrying straight on into the river.*

12.3 *Lock-gates to Port Deauville.*

12.4 *Inside the lock the visitors' berths are all against the breakwater.*

12.5   Typical view of property development within Port Deauville.

12.6   Fishermen alongside the boulevard at Trouville.

12.7   Berths inside the Bassin des Yachts with Trouville Casino beyond.

12.8 *The footbridge separating the Bassin des Yachts with the Bassin Morny.*

12.9 *Deauville yacht club in the Bassin Morny.*

VQ (9) 10s in position 280° 1 mile from outer western breakwater.

Berthing and Facilities

Port Deauville Turn to starboard around the Iso G 4s Lt on a G mast at the end of the mole, giving a wide berth to port to the Q G Lt, then keep parallel to the mole (Digue Brise-Lames) in a buoyed channel towards the lock-gates. The lock-keeper can be contacted on Ch 9. R and G lights control movements through the lock, which has a minimum depth of 2m5 in it.

Inside the 900-berth marina, built in among a spectacular property development of holiday apartments, boats up to 4m draught can be accepted.

Up to 100 visiting yachts can berth on the pontoons inside the mole on your starboard hand after clearing the locks. If relying on walking to the facilities of Port Deauville you should get as far inshore as possible. Otherwise negotiate a vacant berth in the main part of the harbour—or use an outboard to get to the shops and restaurants which are all at the NE corner of the development in the Bassin Central.

Facilities in Port Deauville include a travel-hoist and boatyard alongside the lock. Fuel, FW and electricity are all available.

Bassin des Yachts and Bassin Morny While it is possible to dry out alongside the wall on the E side of the river immediately south of Pointe de la Cahotte, it is best to await the signal on the mast and go straight into the first basin (±2h on HW approx).

12.10   There are some pontoon berths at the inshore end of the Bassin Morny. Trouville Casino in the background.

Visitors are expected to lie stern to the wall on the E side of the Bassin des Yachts, but space can sometimes be found on the pontoons there.

During the shoulder season or by pre-arrangements with the DYC, it is possible to pass through into the Bassin Morny and berth in a more convenient spot for getting to the town and enjoying the warm hospitality and excellent facilities of the clubhouse. The footbridge over the entrance will open on demand. Fuel and FW are available.

Contacts   The HM (on the W bank of the river where it curves away to the left), tel. (31) 88–28–71.

Customs (near the SNCF station just by the bridge to Trouville), tel. (31) 88–63–49.

Port Deauville HO tel. (31) 88–56–16.

Weather on demand by tel. (31) 88–84–22. Area 10 Manche est.

DYC tel. (31) 88–38–19 or 00.

Communications

Regular flights to London or Jersey.

Turbo-train to Paris 2h.

Bus to Le Havre 1¾h, thence ferry to Southampton or Portsmouth 7h.

Charts *BA 1349, 1821 ; Fr 891 ; Im C32 ; (Stan 1)*
High Water *−01h 50 Dover −00h 25 SP Le Havre*
Heights above Datum *Springs MHW 7m5 LMW 0m8*
Neaps MHW 6m2 MLW 2m6

OUISTREHAM lies at the mouth of the 8-mile deep-water canal which runs parallel to the R. Orne from the cathedral city of Caen. It was the scene of the most bitter resistance put up by the Germans following the D-day landings in 1944. The British airborne drop, which secured the beachhead by taking the vital bridge 4km upstream, is commemorated by being named Pegasus Bridge to this day.

Oceangoing ships up to 220m long can pass through the new western lock, with the approach channel dredged to 3m at LW. Yachts can get as far as the lock-gates in any state of the tide.

Approach The flat area of Ouistreham with its beach resort Riva-Bella on the western side of the canal entrance is dominated by the imposing main lighthouse situated immediately to the east of both locks. It is 38m high, W with a R top. The Lt is Oc WR 4s, the R sector covering shoals and rocks off Riva-Bella. Its range is 17 miles.

The main fairway should be picked up 2½ miles to seaward, where a RWVS whistle buoy marked OC is the point at which merchantmen pick up pilots. The light characteristics are Iso 4s. It is perfectly safe to approach at night, but there can be a big swell in the Channel in a northerly blow.

Course 187° for 1 mile passes between two spar buoys: No. 1 is Fl G 4s, while the R No. 2 is Fl R 4s. By night this course is on a leading line with two R Oc (1 + 3) 12s Lts in line. Both are on lattice metal pylons with R tops. The inshore one is twice

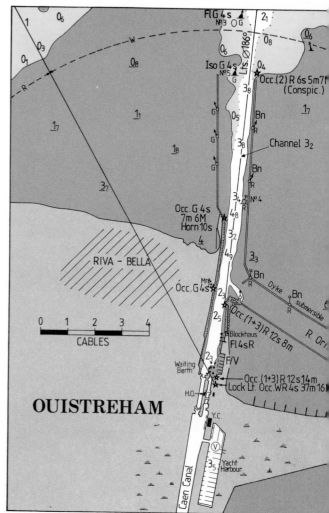

13.1   Double locks leading into Caen Canal with a cut through the east bank to the yacht harbour. Riva-Bella resort to right River Orne to left of picture.

13.2 *Main lighthouse with lock control immediately left of a sizeable ship in the lock.*

as high above sea level at 17m. The channel is well buoyed. Both breakwaters are submerged at high tides from a point well inshore to 6 cables out. The port-hand sunk breakwater is marked by a R tower beacon 16m tall (Oc (2) R 6s 8M). This is Digue Est.

Half a mile farther on is the visible end of the W breakwater (pic 13.1) which is an equally imposing W structure G top on a dolphin. Its Lt is Iso G 4s. It also has a foghorn 10s during the top half of the tide.

The entrance to the R. Orne is off to port, marked by R beacons from No.4 buoy onward. Watch out for dredgers at work.

The Locks Pontoons for boats to lie alongside temporarily while waiting for the locks are on each side, although those on the E side are usually taken up by fishing boats.

The impressive new lock control building between the two locks is where the HO and the HM can be found. Contact on VHF Ch 16, 12 or 68. There are tide gauges and visual displays for depths above datum and controlling traffic in accordance with French standard procedures (see p. 15).

By day and night there are light traffic signals for each lock:
R allows a designated ship to sail outward
G for inward traffic
W Lt under either of the others allows boats under 25m in length to enter or leave

The locks normally operate ±2h of HW, except during July and August when they add at least another hour at either side of the tide.

Berthing

Yacht Harbour Just south of the locks in the Caen Canal there is a narrow cut through the eastern bank leading to a well-sheltered 650-berth marina surrounded by avenues of trees. The clubhouse of the Société des Régates de Caen-Ouistreham (SRCO) is at the NW end of the marina near a launching ramp. Visiting yachts should make for the pontoons on the eastern bank directly opposite the entrance and alongside the slipway.

Facilities Around the Yacht Hbr there are boat agencies, chandlers and a boatyard which can handle most problems.

13.3   Yacht harbour seen from the slip by the yacht club.

Ouistreham village has little to offer. To get to the majority of shops and restaurants, it is necessary to walk across the lock-gates to the Riva-Bella side.

There are FW and electricity at the pontoons, fuel on the canal side of the yacht harbour.

Telephone enquiries about the Yacht Hbr are on (31) 97–19–46. The HM, to whom a flight plan for going on up the canal to Caen should be submitted (to pre-arrange having the bridges open), can be contacted on (31) 97–14–43.

The Customs are on the west bank (tel. (31) 97–18–62).

Weather (31) 74–74–74 (Area 10 Manche est).

CAEN   This city of 125,000 inhabitants is redolent of history—much of it violent—from William the Conqueror and his Queen Matilda to some of the bloodiest battles of the Second World War. Three-quarters of the city was laid waste or put to the torch during June 1944, which proved literally to be the turning-point in the liberation of France. But, like St Malo, it has all been rebuilt in local stone, and the abbeys, churches and museums are open for business.

The passage from Ouistreham can safely be made by the canal. The depth is 9m. Since it is a straightforward keep-in-the-middle passage the bridges will open by pre-arrangement if one sticks

13.4   Cut through from Caen Canal.

13.5   The 'usual facilities' by the visitors' berths directly opposite cut through from the Canal.

to plan, not exceeding the 7-knot speed limit and has pre-paid for the privilege. If bound upstream, give way to vessels proceeding towards the sea.

The bridges are at the following distances upstream from the locks at Ouistreham:

Bénouville 2½ miles,
Hérouville 5¼ miles,
Calix 6½ miles.

Each bridge shows a G Lt when it is clear to pass through.

Once inside the city limits, follow the canal to the swing bridge at La Fondaric where the Bassin St Pierre provides alongside berths for 125 yachts drawing up to 4m, about half of them on pontoons. The harbour authority is near by (tel. (31) 82-12-88).

As a commercial port, the seat of the Prefecture of Calvados and a major tourist attraction, the town can offer all that a boat or her crew might need — if they want to be in the heart of a city.

If a local shipping forecast should be needed before departure there is a continuous taped message (tel. (31) 74-74-74) or a report can be obtained on VHF Ch 12 or 68.

The local YC (Société Nautique de Caen et du Calvados — SNCC) is at 132 Rue Basse and the Calvados Motor YC is in the Hotel Malherbe near the race course.

Caen is served by express trains to Paris in 2h.

*14 COURSEULLES

Charts *BA 1349, 1821 ; Fr 5598 ; Im C32 ; (CG 527)*
High Water *—02h 20 Dover   —00h 30 SP Le Havre*
Heights above Datum *Springs MHW 7m0   MLW 0m8*
          Neaps MHW 5m6   MLW 2m3

TWENTY miles W of Deauville and 9 miles beyond Ouistreham the river Seulles runs into the sea at the point where British forces landed on Juno Beach in June 1944. Nowadays its beaches are popular for other reasons, and it has developed as a holiday centre. There are two Yacht Hbrs: one in the middle of the town (Bassin à Flot) and one as an integral part of a property development (the Nouveau Bassin). The latter is a scaled-down version of the Deauville set-up.

14.1   The new yacht harbour is to the right, alongside the River Seulles. Access is through a swing-bridge (A). The main yacht harbour (Bassin à Flot) is right ahead through lock-gates.

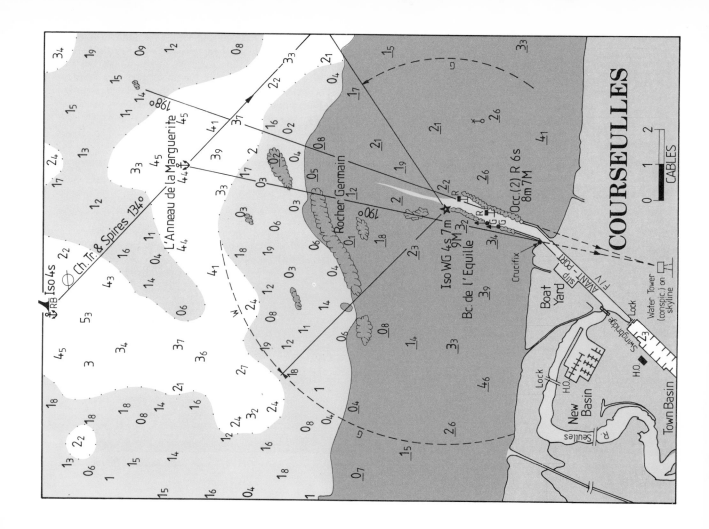

COURSEULLES

CABLES

L'Anneau de la Marguerite

Ch. Tr. & Spires 134°

Iso 4s

RB

Rocher Germain

Bc. de l'Equille

Iso WG 4s 7m 9M 3₂

Occ.(2) R 6s 8m 7M

Crucifix

Boat Yard

AVANT - PORT

F/V

New Basin

Lock

H.O.

Lock

R. Seulles

Swingbridge

H.O.

Water Tower (conspic.) on skyline

Lock

Town Basin

1980

190

14.2   *Marks at the harbour entrance.*

14.3   *Gate and lock control ahead. The swing-bridge into the Nouveau Bassin can be seen to the right.*

14.4 Nouveau Bassin within property development.

Approach Outside the lock-gates the Avant-Port dries at LWS out to a distance of ½ mile to seaward. The leading marks are the spires of the church la Déliverande 1½ miles inshore on the hilltop in transit with the church at Bernières on the coast 1 mile east of Courseulles. A course of 134° takes the inward-bound yacht in deep water to the RWVS spar buoy (Iso 4s) just one mile NxW of the pierhead. There is good holding ground in its immediate vicinity, if waiting for the tide.

For longer-range identification there is the lighthouse at Ver, 2 miles west of Courseulles, a W tower with Grey top at 42m elevation Fl (3) 15s with a range of 17 miles. It also has a 20-mile Radio Beacon on 219.9kHz (callsign "ÉR" · · — · · · — ·).

From the fairway buoy leave the transit of churches and head 170° towards the dolphin with a G-topped wooden framework

1½ cables to seaward of the western breakwater and separated from it by two G beacons in line. The light is Iso WG 4s to a range of 9 miles. The white sector shows between 135° and 235°, with G on either side covering the rocks. It sounds a horn ev 30s in fog.

At the root of the western breakwater there is a prominent crucifix which, brought into line with a conspicuous water tower behind the town on 190°, provides an alternative approach within 2h of HW.

The end of the E breakwater has a similar light structure with a R top. Its Lt is Oc (2) R 6s. It also has two unlit beacons marking its seaward extension. This brought into transit with the Iso W, mentioned above, on course 187° can be used as a lead-in at night, always remembering the unlit beacons. The deepest part

14.5 *Bassin à Flot above the locks. Bureau du Port and most facilities are on the right bank.*

of the channel at entry is nearer the eastern side (pic 14.2).

Berthing Once inside the Avant-Port there are drying berths alongside the eastern side. The opposite bank is mostly taken up by a long slipway in front of the boatyard. Just beyond this hard the R. Seulles runs into the Avant-Port under a swing-bridge which opens on demand up to ±3h on HW depending on tidal height.

The entrance to the New Harbour is over a sill on the S side of a mole down the middle of the river (3m3). Boats drawing 1m50 can lie alongside the pontoons there. This little marina has its own HO at the western end.

The better bet, guaranteeing a least depth of 2m3, is through the lock-gates in the Bassin à Flot. The pontoons on the western side are most suitable for visitors, with the HO on the quayside.

Some belong to the local YC—Société des Régates de Courseulles (SRC) whose clubhouse is on the eastern side of the basin (Quai Est).

Facilities There is a yacht agency and chandlery, called Serra Marine, on the Quai Ouest, which can do all servicing and afloat repairs.

FW at the pontoons. Fuel at the Quai Ouest.

For berthing reservations or enquiries about lock and swing bridge opening call (31) 97–46–03, or check at the new lock control office on the western side of lock.

Weather is posted at the HO. Area 10 Manche est.

The town has all the amenities one would expect of a somewhat up-market holiday resort, including one memorable fish restaurant and a number of hotels.

Charts   *Fr 5515 ; BA 1821 ; (Im C32 ; CG 527)*
High Water   *−02h 15 Dover   −00h 45 SP Le Havre*
Heights above Datum   *Springs   MHW 7m2   MLW 1m1*
                                     Neaps   MHW 6m0   MLW 2m6

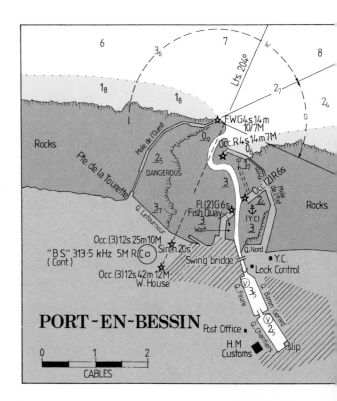

PORT-EN-BESSIN is an important fishing port and a harbour for coastal traffic. There are limited berths for visiting yachts who don't stay too long. It lies between the cliffs half-way from Cour-seulles to Grandcamp, close west of Arromanches and the D-day Gold Beach. One of its attractions is in that it is the nearest Yacht Hbr to Bayeux with its famous cathedral and museum with the anonymous cartoon-tapestry immortalising the Norman invasion of Britain in 1066.

Approach   Entry should not be attempted in heavy weather from the N or NE or before half-tide, even though there is over 2m0 right up to the outer breakwaters. The leading marks are a W house (42m) beyond a W tower on 204°. Both are Oc (3) 12s and the front one has a siren ev 20s. On the western side of the town there is a Radio Beacon (continuous transmission on 313.5kHz, callsign "BS" with a range of 5 miles).

After passing between the breakwaters (Oc R 4s on a R tower to port and Fl WG 4s to starboard—the G sector covers the rocks close inshore) it is best to make for the inner harbour because the outer harbour dries out on its western side at LW springs. Its pierheads have lights Oc (2) R 6s and Fl (2) G 6s on either side. A R-topped beacon marks the end of a submerged break-water to port. Once inside, the moorings on one's port hand are all privately owned by the local YC—Centre Nautique de Port-en-Bessin (CNPB)—which is located near the eastern side of the lock-gates leading to the inner basin.

15.1   Berths inside inner breakwater on the port hand all belong to the yacht club and dry out. Lock is open. Yachts all berthed beyond old (now removed) lock on the east side.

The best place to wait is inside the seaward end of western inner quay, where a coastal vessel is seen in the accompanying aerial picture (15.1). Here it also dries at LWS, but there is a minimum of 1m50 at LWN.

There is a swing-bridge across the outer end of the cut leading to the lock, which is supposed to open for 5 min on the hour and half hour during ±2h of HW, which are the advertised times of the lock opening. The bridge has R Lts to show when it is shut. A prolonged hoot on a horn might also do the trick.

A R Lt or R flag indicates that ships may not enter the basin. G Lt or flag means no departure. R over G means no movement either way.

15.2 Open lock-gates and bridge from seaward.

15.3 Fishing boats berthed on west side just above lock. Disused lock in background.

The lock control is on the eastern side (tel. (31) 21–71–77).

Berthing and Facilities In theory yachts may berth on either side just beyond the farthest piers inside the 500m length of the basins. The picture (15.1) shows yachts lying on the eastern side, while fishing boats tend to hog the other side, which is the more attractive for being nearest the shops and bars. However it is always possible to talk an obliging fisherman into a berth outboard of his boat. The basins are maintained at 2m50 minimum depth.

There is a slip and boatyard at the head of the basin.

The HO and Customs are at the town end of the fishmarket tel. (31) 21–70–49.

Weather is taped on (31) 74–74–74 or may be obtained at 0633 and 1133 on VHF Ch3. Area 10 Manche est.

*16 GRANDCAMP-MAISY

Charts *Fr 847 ; BA 2073 ; (CG 527)*
High Water *−02h 20 Dover*
  −01h HW   −00h 30 LW SP Le Havre
Heights above Datum *Springs   MHW 7m8   MLW 1m1*
  Neaps   MHW 6m5   MLW 2m8

GRANDCAMP is a fishing port 4 miles west of Omaha Beach, which has recently developed successfully into being a Yacht Hbr and holiday centre with some elegant apartments built around the western half of the harbour. The eastern and southern quays are reserved for the considerable fishing fleet. The latter is the site of a large modern fishmarket.

Approach A rocky outcrop extends for a mile offshore, but it can safely be negotiated on the leading line at any time the lock-gates are open (normally ±2½h on HW). The timing of opening the lock-gates is governed by the tides at Dunkerque (open at LW and shut at HW!).

The best approach is from a point midway between the two westernmost unlit N-cardinal buoys, to seaward of the rocks (Nos3 and 5). The course is 146° right for the pierheads. Off the end of the eastern jetty there is a W column with R top (Oc (2) R 6s); the other pierhead has a W column with a G top (Fl G 4s). The leading lights are both Q W, visible 10° either side of the 146° course.

It is not feasible to anchor short of the lock or to enter in a northerly blow.

Berthing There are 300 pontoon berths with a least depth of 2m50. 20 are reserved for visiting yachts at the end of the first E–W pontoon after turning to starboard through the locks. The

16.1 Top part of tide with lock-gates open. Visitors' berths on outer end of main E–W pontoons. Harbour Office next to fishmarket at top right-hand corner of harbour.

16.2 *Through this lock and alter 90° to port for visitors' berths.*

16.3 *New arrivals berth on outboard end of either of these pontoons.*

16.4 *Extra pontoons for shoal draft boats. Harbour entrance in the background.*

HO (tel. (31) 22–62–16) is at the SW corner of the harbour, next to the fishmarket.

Facilities There is a YC Cercle Nautique de Grandcamp-les-Bains (CNG)—on the Quai Crampon (NE corner of harbour) open only in the season and weekends. Bathroom facilities at the HO.

FW and electricity on the pontoons. Fuel at the eastern fish quay (Henri Chéron).

There is a boatyard where all repairs can be made.

Provisioning is adequate. Bistros not too plentiful or classy. Yacht chandlery near the HO.

Weather is posted at the lock and the Bureau du Port. Area 10 Manche est.

*17 ISIGNY-SUR-MER

Charts *BA 2073 ; Fr 847 ; (CG 527)*
High Water *+01h (approx) Cherbourg*
Heights above Datum *Springs MHW 7m30 MLW zero*
                          Neaps MHW 6m00 MLW zero

ISIGNY lies 5 miles to the E of Carentan and has a much shorter and deeper channel to the open sea. But it is only of interest to boats prepared to dry out alongside the town quay. There is no lock and the navigable part of the river ends at the bridge in the centre of town (pic 17.2).

Approach As for Carentan, except that the course from the E Cardonnet buoy is 235° to pick up the whistling RWVS pillar buoy IS. If coming from the E it is necessary to keep to seaward of the three N-cardinal buoys marking the shoal water and rocks off Grandcamp. In a heavy blow from the NW access is not recommended.

There is a buoyed channel taking one on course 200° until picking up the leading marks on 173° to pass between a G-topped beacon to starboard and a R beacon to port. The latter marks the eastern side of the straight channel 1½ miles long to the river junction.

At this point the W beacon which carries the front leading light (Oc (1+2) 12s) is conspicuous and should be left to starboard as course is altered to port to enter the last short reach to the town. The rear light on a 23m W metal framework with a B top has the same light characteristics and range (18M). The leading lights are intensified in the sector 171°–175°.

Berthing The scene is not unlike Sandwich. The best berth is on the pontoons on the west side (pic 17.1) but it is also possible

17.1 A few alongside berths on the west bank. Even the pontoon is aground.

17.2 End of navigable water at bridge in mid town.

to dry out on the quay on the opposite bank nearer the bridge. FW and fuel are available.

The local harbour authority is at 5 Rue Hogues (tel. (31) 22–03–11), where the weather is posted. Area 10 Manche est.

Facilities There is a local boatbuilder and a garage with yacht mechanics. Good shopping, hotels and restaurants.

*18 CARENTAN

Charts   *BA 2073 ; Fr 847 ; (Im C32 ; CG 527)*
High Water   *+01h (approx) Cherbourg*
Heights above Datum   *Springs   MHW 4m10 MLW 2m10*
                          Neaps   MLW as datum

CARENTAN is a market town 4½ miles inland from the head of the Baie du Grand Vey, which lies at the western end of the D-day beaches.

An imposing church (mostly twelfth century) dominates the scene. It also features a fifteenth-century covered market with Gothic archways. For yachtsmen there is perfect shelter provided by the newly furnished marina. It is a good jumping-off point to cruise to the Îles St Marcouf, which are only 8 miles distant from the seaward end of the Carentan Canal. Grandcamp, St Vaast and Port-en-Bessin are within easy reach, while Honfleur is only 55 miles to the E.

Approach   Do not attempt entry by night. Some 5 miles SSE of Îles St Marcouf or the same distance from the E-cardinal buoy marking the eastern extremity of the Cardonnet Bank (BYB Q Fl (3) 5s) on a course of 255° find the RWVS spar buoy with a R disc topmark marked "CA". It lies 3 miles to seaward of the canal entrance. It is a whistle buoy.

The inward channel is well buoyed, with 10 unlit G buoys to starboard and 9 R to port. As the local chart warns, this channel may vary according to shifting sand banks. In 1984 the initial course down the fairway was 195°, while leading lights are on 210°. The front Lt is Oc (3) R 12s with high intensity in the arc 207°–213° out to a range of 14 miles. Its structure is a 6m W post with a R top.

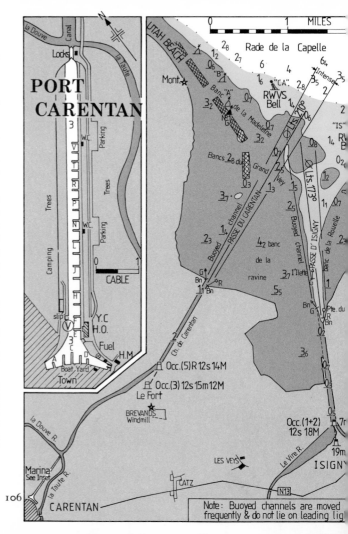

18.1   Lock-gates leading into Port of Carentan.

The synchronised rear Lt is on a 15m W column with a G top. Its light is Oc (3) W 12s with a range of 12 miles. Both lights lie on the E bank of the canal, the front one being 1½ miles from the canal entrance.

On passing between buoys Nos 9 and 10 alter to 245° to head for the canal entrance between G and R top-marked beacons; thereafter the course is 210°.

Depths   At LWS the whole approach route dries out to within half a mile of the Carentan buoy. The shallowest point is in the canal entrance where it dries 2m2, so care must be taken during neaps when access may be restricted to boats drawing less than 1m50. Ideally one should leave the CA buoy inward-bound 1½h before HW.

Two miles beyond the front leading light one reaches the confluence of the rivers Taute and Douve which encircle the town.

Entrance   The lock-gates are right ahead. Notionally they open 2h either side of HW, but it is as well to check with the HO on Ch9 or tel. (33) 42-24-24. Off-season they sometimes do not open during the night. You can write to PO Box 104, Bureau du Port, Carentan, Normandie, for a complete schedule of times of opening and shutting for the whole year, including graphs to show hours of access for boats up to 3m50 draught.

Berthing   The locks keep a level of 5m inside the last ¾ mile of the canal, which has now been furnished as a 530-berth marina. Since there are towpaths on each side by the magnificent elm trees there is a lot of room for increasing the capacity (rather like Vannes). At present there are eighteen pontoons anchored to the E bank and another four across the head of the canal. Visitors should berth near the HO and YC (CN Carentais) located at pontoon E, the last one on the port hand after entry. Tel. (33) 42-04-11. Weather posted there. Area 10 Manche est.

18.2 *Pontoon berths downstream from the yacht club.*

18.3 *Berths nearest the town at the head of the harbour.*

Facilities Water and electricity are available on the pontoons. Fuel is just around the head of the harbour to port, near the boatyard. All repairs can be carried out. There are a 15-ton lift and two slipways.

Excellent hotels and restaurants. Good for shopping, including chandlery.

SNCF train to Paris St Lazare in $2\frac{1}{2}$h.

*19 ST VAAST-LA-HOUGUE

Charts   *BA 1349; Fr 5522; (CG 528; Im C32; BA 2073)*
High Water   −02h 20 Dover   +01h 00 SP Cherbourg
Heights above Datum   *Springs*   MHW 6m5   MLW 0m9
                                      Neaps   MHW 5m3   MLW 2m3

ST VAAST has been transformed since its harbour has been dredged, lock-gates installed and a 730-berth marina completed with a least depth 2m3 maintained at all times (1983). The old town forms one side of the Yacht Hbr and has a succession of attractive little stores and bistros, many of them featuring the local oysters for which St Vaast is famous. It is also an excellent place to stock up with wines from the extensive caves. The tiny Chapelle des Marins overlooks the harbour entrance. Inside are memorials to many local sailors lost in recent times.

Approach   There is ample water to within ½ mile SSE of the breakwater. Thereafter it shoals rapidly and dries out for a distance of 2 cables on the same line.

The lock-gates open and shut at half-tide with some local variations. A straightforward R or G traffic Lt at the lock entrance controls entry or exit. The HO is on your starboard side alongside the gate. It can be contacted on Ch9, or tel. (33) 54–43–61.

From the SSE   St Vaast is protected from the NE by the Île de Tatihou lying ½ mile off the entrance with a prominent seventeenth-century round tower (with a small lookout tower on its left-hand side). There is a similar tower at Fort de la Hougue, the isthmus south of the village. The fairway lies between these two on a course of 349°, with the left-hand edge of Tatihou in transit with the steeple of Réville village.

On this course the two S-cardinal buoys 6 cables SE of Tatihou

marking La Dent and Le Gavendest rocks are left to starboard, while on the port hand the E-cardinal buoys Le Manquet (½ mile to seaward and due E of the tip of Fort de la Hougue) and Le Bout du Roc are left to port. Also left to port is the beacon on Le Creux de Bas rocks. All these marks are unlit.

The outer end of the breakwater has an Oc (4) WR 6s on a W tower with a R top 11m high. It has a siren (N 30s). Rounding the breakwater shape 270° for the entrance proper, with a W pedestal and a G top to starboard (Iso 6 4s) and a W hut with R roof to port (Oc 4 R 12s). The lock-gates are then immediately ahead.

From the East   The left-hand edge of Fort de la Hougue is brought in transit with the W octagonal lighthouse 90m above sea level at Morsalines on course 267°. The front Lt is Oc (2) W 6s; the Morsalines light is Oc (1+3) WRG 12s, but only the W sector will be seen on the correct approach. This will bring you 2 cables S of La Dent, after which alter to starboard and join the approach transit from the SSE as described above.

Berthing   In settled weather a good anchorage can be found W of La Dent, for example, to wait for the tide. Although fishing boats may be lying alongside the S breakwater, the small cut immediately inside the entrance is reserved for the lifeboat and the slipways of the yacht yard.

Visiting yachts should go alongside any of the first three pontoons (A, B or C). The first two are designed for larger boats, with 8m fingers and 3m3 depth of water. The town side of the marina is reserved for fishing boats and other commercial craft.

Facilities   On the reclaimed land at the head of the pontoons there is a magnificent new clubhouse (Cercle Nautique de la Hougue) with ample car parking and winter berths ashore. There is a travel lift at the N end of the Yacht Hbr. FW and electricity are available at every berth, but in 1983 diesel was not available in the Marina.

The boatyard near the little church on the S side of the lock-

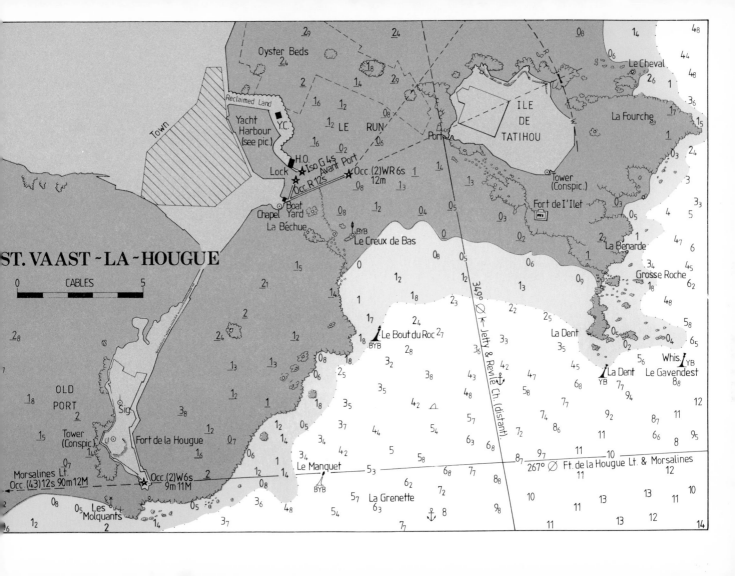

19.1 *Shot of the new (1983) marina taken from the NW with Tatihou Island in the background. The yacht club is at (A), the Bureau du Port and open lock-gates at (B). Approach course is indicated.*

19.2   Harbour entrance from seaward with lock shut. Yacht yard and chandlery to the right of the inshore end of the breakwater ; the Chapelle des Marins to the left.

19.3   The old quayside within the new yacht harbour, now used by fishing boats.

gates seems to be efficiently run and has a well-stocked chandlery including charts.

The Customs are on Rue Marechal Foch (tel. (33) 54–43–00). There is a good bus service to Valognes 17km away, which lies on the main railway line from Cherbourg to Paris.

The HA is on tel. (33) 54–43–61.

Weather is posted at the Bureau du Port and at the YC. Area 10 Manche est.

*20 BARFLEUR

Charts   *BA 1349, 2073 ; Fr 5618 ; (Im C32)*
High Water   *− 2h 30 Dover   + 01h 00 SP Cherbourg*
Heights above Datum   *Springs   MHW 6m5   MLW 1m2*
                          Neaps   MHW 5m3   MLW 2m5

A MOST attractive little fishing village situated 2 miles south of Cap Barfleur with its imposing lighthouse 71m tall alongside the remains of an earlier structure (pic 20.1). The harbour dries out completely, but along the quayside (Quai Henri Chardon) and anywhere in the NW half of the harbour the bottom is suitable for taking the ground. Its popularity with visiting British yachts may diminish now that the new marina at near-by St Vaast-la-Hougue is complete. It is also exposed to E and NE'ly winds.

Approach   From whatever direction one approaches give Cap Barfleur a wide berth and be sure to consult the tidal atlas. The currents run up to 4 knots and a race develops E of the lighthouse especially when the N'going tide sweeping out of the Baie de la Seine from −03h 20 HW Dover meets the main E–W stream off the tip of the peninsula. I once kedged off Barfleur and took twenty-eight mackerel in as many minutes. The main Lt is Fl (2) 10s with a range of 27 miles. Its foghorn is two 2s blasts in a 60s cycle. The Radio Beacon ("FG" callsign) on 291.9kHz has a 70-mile range and is the strongest of its group, which is Cap d'Antifer, St Catherine's and Portland Bill.

Keep a mile offshore until the G unlit buoy with cone topmark to the E of La Grotte rocks is sighted. Come on to a SW'ly course so as to pass between another G buoy (Roches des Anglais) and a R one with can topmark to port, marking the offshore extremity

20.1   *Cap Barfleur lighthouse. Note the overfalls and calmer seas towards Barfleur port.*

Ø 219°

20.2 *The port at 1½h before HW. Transit 219° is shown. Harbour Office (A) will direct visitors to the drying-out alongside berth on quayside. It is easy to see the areas where it is not suitable to dry out—there are no boats there.*

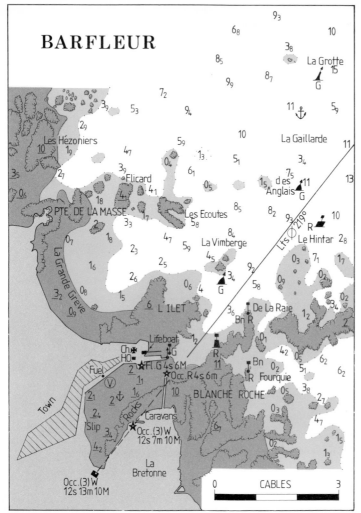

20.3 *Inshore end of the lead-in transit.*

of the rocks at Le Hintar. Course should now be 219° in transit with 2 square W Lt towers. On the leading marks there is a least depth of 4m5 to within 1 cable of the entrance at LW. The forward one (7m high) is in a caravan park. The rear one is 13m high and has a G top on a square structure built above a prominent house at the head of the harbour (pic 20.2). Both are Oc (3) 12s and are synchronised with one another. The harbour dries out to 2m4 above datum in the half suitable for taking the ground.

Course 219° heads just to the left of the harbour entrance. La Vimberge rocks to starboard are marked by another G cone-topped buoy just 3 cables short of the harbour. At this point the bottom shoals rapidly and it is advisable to lie off or anchor until 2h before HW, when it is possible to enter. There are some small moorings just off the fairway which are reserved for local fishing boats. The southern breakwater shows Oc R 4s at its extremity,

20.4 Front transit light almost in line with picture 20.3.

20.5 Harbour entrance.

20.6 *The Harbour Office is the white hut in front of the church. Note the end of the slipway still not covered by tide.*

20.7 *Alongside berths at Quai Henri Chardon.*

just off the main approach transit. The inner breakwater (to starboard) has a Fl G 4s, 7m.

Berthing The best berths are alongside the quay on the starboard hand on entering, although the HM, whose office is next to the YC at the head of the slip inside the northern breakwater (tel. (33) 54–43–61), may well direct visiting boats to lie up to four abreast farther inshore. All berths dry 2m.

Facilities Weather is posted at the HO or taped on (33) 53–11–55. Area 10 Manche est.

Barfleur has most things a visiting yachtsman can wish for: water, fuel, good restaurants and bars, all kinds of shops and a garage with yacht mechanics. For the homesick, the main street is named after St Thomas à Becket (Archevèque de Canterbury). The pretty little church by the lifeboat station just N of the entrance has beyond it a delightful bathing beach. There are regular buses to Cherbourg. The nearest Customs are in St Vaast, 6 miles S.

21 CHERBOURG

Charts *BA 2602 ; Fr 5628 ; Im C32 ; CG 528 ; (Stan 1)*
High Water *−03h 20 Dover SP Cherbourg*
Heights above Datum *Springs MHW 6m8 MLW 0m5*
Neaps MHW 4m8 MLW 2m8

CHERBOURG lies in the middle of the shallow bay between Cap de la Hague in the W and Cap Barfleur to the E. The outer harbour (Grande Rade) which is inshore of the detached breakwater (Digue Centrale) and two moles (Digue de Querqueville and Digue de l'Est) is nearly as big as Portland and Plymouth Sound put together, being about 4 miles E–W and one mile N–S. The inner harbour (Petite Rade) is surrounded by the town of 90,000 inhabitants, which owes its existence to the massive artificial harbours dating back to Louis XVI's time, although not completed until Napoleon III in 1853 followed five years later by the opening of the naval dockyard.

The Petite Rade is divided into three zones, each mutually exclusive to their users. The western end forms the naval base and dockyard, where nuclear submarines and frigates are built. The eastern part is the commercial port, with the faded glory of the old transatlantic passenger terminal (the first scheduled service to USA started in 1869) now used mainly by ferries from Southampton or Portsmouth. On reclaimed land farther E massive offshore oil platforms are built and launched. The museum in Fort du Roule with its commanding view of the whole area from 112m up is worth a visit.

In between these two areas a 630-boat marina (Port de Plaisance Chantereyne) has been built with every conceivable facility on tap. It is now the only place where visiting yachts may lie. The old Yacht Hbr farther inshore is reserved for a few local boats, including fishermen. The old YC is shut and abandoned. Most of the traditional bars and restaurants are now a taxi-ride away.

Outside the Straits of Dover, Cherbourg is the closest French port to the South Coast, only an overnight trip of 60 miles from the Needles, 84 miles from Torbay or 90 from Brighton. It is accessible at all states of the tide and affords excellent shelter from any direction.

21.1 Light at the east end of Digue Centrale with Fort Centrale to the right. The west entrance is 3.7km away at the far end of this massive breakwater.

119

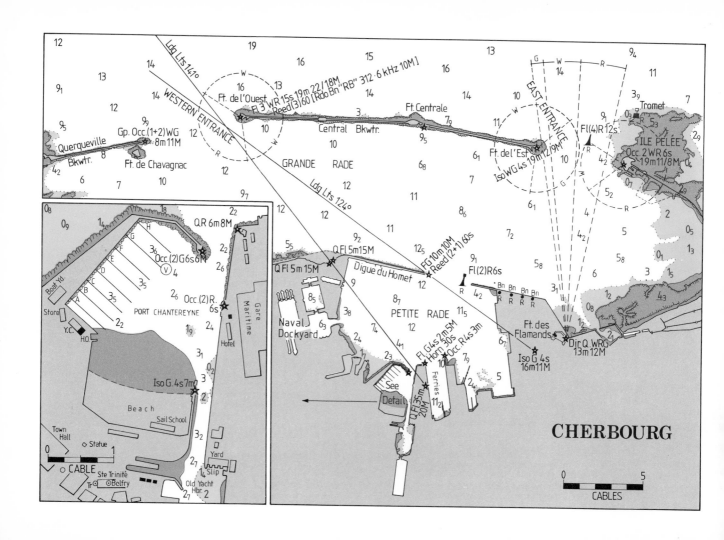

12

19

13

14   Ldg Lts 141°

9₁

16

16

15

13

9₄

9₃

14

14   WESTERN ENTRANCE

Ft. de l'Ouest

13

14

G   W   R

14

11

13

Querqueville

9₅

Gp. Occ.(1+2)WG
8m11M

9₉

12

Fl 3 WR 15s 19m 22/18M
Reed(3)60 [Rdo Bn "RB" 312·6 kHz 10M]

14

16

EAST ENTRANCE

Tromet

3₉

7

2₉

Bkwtr.   8

Ft. de Chavagnac

10

Ft. Centrale

14

10

Fl(4)R 12s

0₃

5₃

4₂

12

10

3

Central   Bkwtr.

9₅

7₉

11

9₁

R

ÎLE PELÉE
Occ. 2 WR 6s
19m11/8M

0₅

4₂

6

7

10

GRANDE   RADE

10

6₈

Ft. de l'Est
IsoWG4s 19m12/9M

6₁

10

5₂

0₁

2₉

12

12

11

8₆

7₂

6₁

4₂

5

5₈

6

0₁

1₃

0₈

0₉

18

2₂

QR 6m8M

12

12

11

9₂

QFl 5m15M

FG 10m10M
Reed (2+1) 60s

12₅

9₁

5₈

4₂

3₁

1₂

5

4₃

H

G

3₆

Occ.(2)G6s6M

2₂

2₆

5₅

QFl 5m 15M

Digue du Homet

Fl(2)R6s

R

Bn Bn Bn Bn
R R R R

0₈

F

E

D

C
B
A

3₅

Ⓥ 4

2₆

Occ.(2)R.
6s

8₅

8₇

PETITE RADE

11₅

4₂

1₂

2₄

Boat Yd

Store

Y.C.
H.O.

2₂

1₉

PORT CHANTEREYNE

Gare
Maritime

Naval
Dockyard

6₃

3₈

7₄

12

6₁

Ft. des
Flamands

1₂

2₁

Dir Q. WRG
13m12M

2₄

Hotel

2₄

2₃

IsoG 4s7m

3₁

3

2

0₂

Beach

Sail School

See
Detail

Fl G4s 2m5M
Horn 30s

Occ.R.4s 3m

7₉

IsoG 4s
16m11M

5

Town
Hall

Statue

3₂

Ferries

11₂

5

CABLE

Ste Trinité
Belfry

Tr

Old Yacht
Hbr. 2

2₇

1₄   Slip

Yard

QFl 35m
20M

11₂

CHERBOURG

0   5

CABLES

21.2 Passing the east end of Digue du Homet into the inner — the whole area to the right of the beacon is forbidden. White buildings are part of the naval base and dockyard.

21.3 Entrance to Chantereyne yacht harbour, with the old transatlantic jetty to the left.

21.4 Inside yacht harbour. Services yacht Dasher *(Nicholson 55, dark hull) lying alongside a visitors' berth on second pontoon from the entrance.*

It deserves to be more popular than it seems to be for visiting British yachts. Those who race on the RORC circuit think of Cherbourg largely in terms of looking in thick fog and a 5-knot spring tide for the CH1 buoy (Oc 4s RW stripes and a whistle which sounds more like a moan) 3½ miles NW of the harbour entrance. Many have spent hours kedged in its vicinity waiting for wind or tide. In the days before the Radio Beacon was established on the western fort, with a notional range of 20 miles, it could be an anxious landfall. Off-lying dangers exist only if one fetches up 5 miles to the eastward—not unheard of. Hence the comments attributed to Uffa Fox while navigating the schooner *Lumberjack* in thick fog. He was woken from a deep sleep to fix the boat's position. He took a sniff to weather and declared them to be just off Cherbourg. Later he attributed this uncanny accuracy to having smelled coal-dust and call-girls.

Another attraction of Cherbourg for British yachts is that it is an excellent, secure harbour in which to wait for the tide in either direction or for the weather to improve. It is also convenient and uncomplicated for storing ship for a cruise to W Cork or S Brittany. Crews joining from UK can use the ferries (4¼h).

Approaches From whichever direction Cherbourg is approached the tidal currents are likely to play a decisive part. If the wind has been blowing for any length of time from W or E it is advisable to put a bit extra in the bank by allowing stronger currents than those predicted. It is never safe to assume on a 12h passage from, say, Poole, that the tides will cancel each other out. If the visibility is not perfect, start checking by D/F bearings when you estimate to be 20 miles offshore using:

Alderney Aerobeacon (callsign "ALD") on 383kHz

Barfleur ("FG") on 219.9kHz

Cherbourg ("RB") on 312.6kHz

The last is relatively weak with a 20-mile range, so may not come up until late in the passage.

In extreme visibility by day Cherbourg will appear to lie in a dip in the skyline with Cap de la Hague forming a prominent right-hand edge of land. Near it is the nuclear power station under construction (1983) whose floodlights are especially prominent by night—rather more so than the loom of the city lights of Cherbourg.

Ferries to or from the Solent may use either entrance to the Grande Rade, but within those limits a chance sighting of one can be reassuring. The W entrance is the more popular, though there is plenty of room through either. The light on Fort de l'Ouest is the most powerful in the locality (Fl (3) 15s) with 22-miles range in its W sector and 18 in the R sector (covering NW-W-S) to prevent a boat coming from the W cutting it too fine off Pointe de Querqueville. There is ample water to within 60yds of the west breakwater where there is a R conical buoy (Oc R 4s) immediately SW of the breakwater extremity to be left to port.

At the eastern entrance it also pays to shape close to the Fort de l'Est, coming in on the W sector of the Iso WG 4s with its 12-mile range. Here the rocky sub-structure of the breakwater extends 100yds to seaward and is unmarked. Approaching from Barfleur/Cap Lévy it is important to give a wide berth to the Île Pelée, the rocky outcrop on which the fort marking the NW extremity of the eastern mole is built. Give a wide berth to the unlit R beacon with can topmark (Tromet) and the R spar buoy (Fl (4) R 12s) marking La Truite and the port hand of the deep channel at the entrance.

Once inside the Grande Rade through either entrance, head straight for the eastern end of the Digue du Homet, the western breakwater guarding the Petite Rade. Its fixed G Lt 10m high forms a transit with an Iso G Lt 4s 16m high on the reclaimed land at the eastern end of the Petite Rade. This transit on 124° brings an inbound ship straight from the western entrance to the Petite Rade. A safe course to pass through the eastern entrance is to stay in the W sector of the Q on the Fort des Flamands at the eastern end of the Petite Rade. Once inside, a course of 220°

21.5 New yacht club building at the town end of the breakwater.

for 1 mile takes you to the entrance of Petite Rade, leaving to port a R spar buoy with topmark (Fl (2) R 6s) off the end of the eastern arm of the breakwater—the Jetée des Flamands.

The twin arms of the old transatlantic jetties with the RO/RO ferry berth at its head are then seen fine on the port bow. Course 200° for 6 cables will bring one to the narrow gap between the seaward end of the breakwater protecting the new Chantereyne marina (Oc (2) G 6s) and the western end of the arm on which the conspicuous Gare Maritime is situated, marked by a QR.

Berthing Swing to starboard round the end of the inner breakwater and head for the visitors' berths on pontoon G—the second one in from the entrance. There is a minimum of 4m

water in the vicinity of the pontoons. It may be permitted to anchor briefly there while getting sorted out; to all intents and purposes neither berthing nor anchoring is allowed anywhere else in Cherbourg. Some charts indicate that the marina is being extended by filling the southern half of the Yacht Hbr with pontoons. But it seems as though the sailing school and its sailboards have taken over the fine sandy beach there (1984).

Port Operation The Marina Office is situated in the same building as the Cherbourg YC (YCC) near the travel-hoist, boatyard, chandlers and ship's stores. It should be contacted on Ch9 or immediately after berthing. The Customs offices there are no longer manned and it is not necessary to contact them

21.6 The old Avant-Port, familiar as Cherbourg's first marina. Old yacht club now boarded up. Berths reserved for locals. Duty-free stores used to be collected from prominent building (centre front). Fort du Roule on the hilltop where last German resistance ended—now a museum of the Second Front.

so long as one's ship's papers (Certificate of Registration) are in order. It is advisable to have valid passports, especially if a visit to the casino is contemplated, and a UK Customs Form C1328, completed before leaving UK.

Facilities Information on every conceivable facility for sustaining a yacht or her crew can be obtained through the Yacht Club de Cherbourg (Ch9 or tel. (33) 52–02–83). Showers and heads are at the inshore end of pontoon C. Windsurfing, dinghy charters or instruction can be arranged through the Cercle Nautique Cherbourgais (CNC) within easy walk of the YCC. There are two other YCs (CNMC and CNEMC) near the mag-

nificent sports complex immediately next to the Yacht Hbr, but they are reserved for French service personnel.

Recorded weather forecasts are obtainable on tel. (33) 53–11–55 or from Radio Brest-Le Conquet (FFU). Cherbourg local weather is on Ch27 VHF at 0633 and 1133. The port lies almost on the dividing line between area 11 (Manche ouest) and area 10 (Manche est).

Local VHF contact for services outside those covered by the HO at the marina should initially be made on Ch16 calling 'COM Cherbourg'.

PART FOUR

CHANNEL ISLANDS AND ADJACENT COAST OF FRANCE

Omonville — Erquy

and tidal charts covering the area

Soundings and heights in cables
Bearings and courses in degrees true
Distances at sea in nautical miles or cables

DISTANCES AROUND THE CHANNEL ISLANDS

Distances shown are safe navigable routes between breakwaters and/or estuary entrances (in nautical miles)

CHERBOURG	CHERBOURG							
ALDERNEY	21	ALDERNEY						
ST PETER PORT	41	23	ST PETER PORT					
ST HELIER	57	40	26	ST HELIER				
CHAUSEY [S]	77	60	48	24	CHAUSEY [S]			
GRANVILLE	83	66	53	29	9	GRANVILLE		
ST MALO	83	66	52	30	15	21	ST MALO	
LÉZARDRIEUX	81	65	41	41	47	56	37	LÉZARDRIEUX

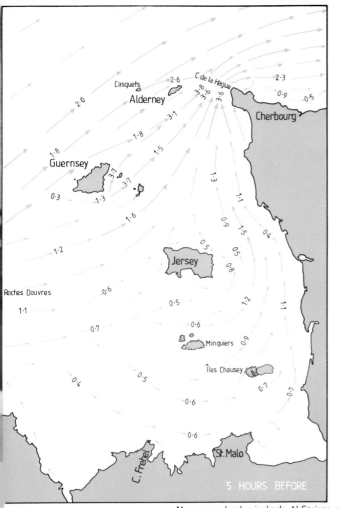

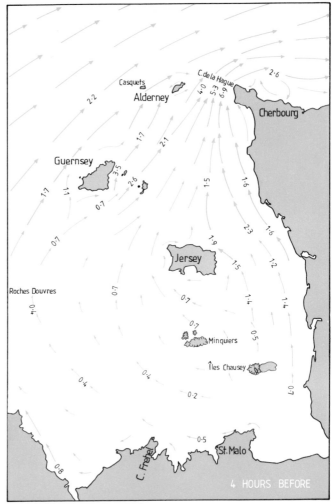

Mean current rates in knots At Springs, add one-third. At Neaps, subtract one-third.

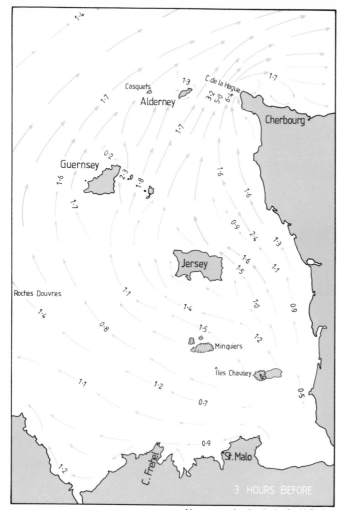

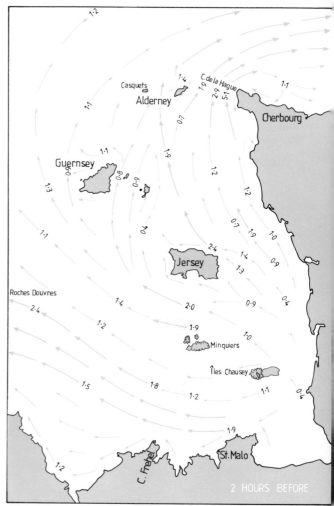

Mean current rates in knots. At Springs, add one-third. At Neaps, subtract one-third.

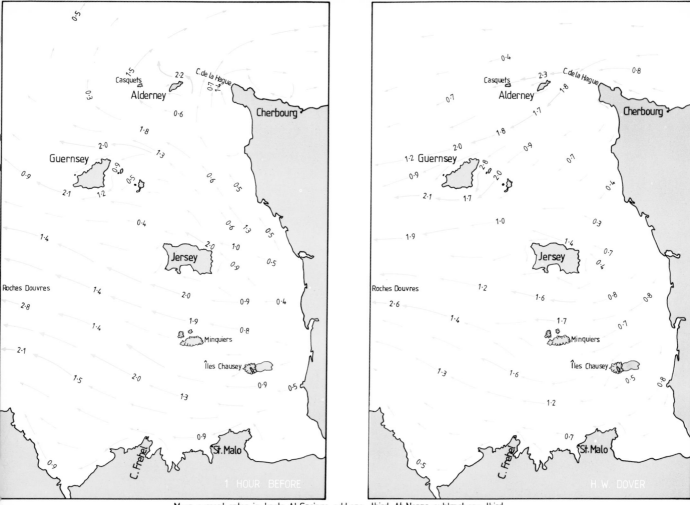

Mean current rates in knots At Springs, add one-third. At Neaps, subtract one-third.

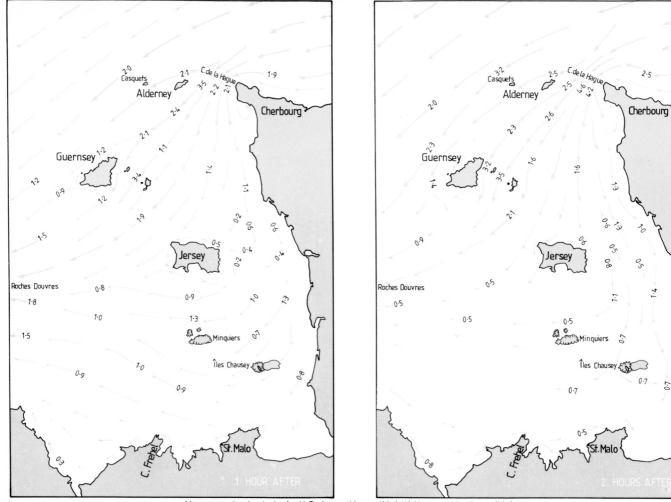

Mean current rates in knots. At Springs, add one-third. At Neaps, subtract one-third.

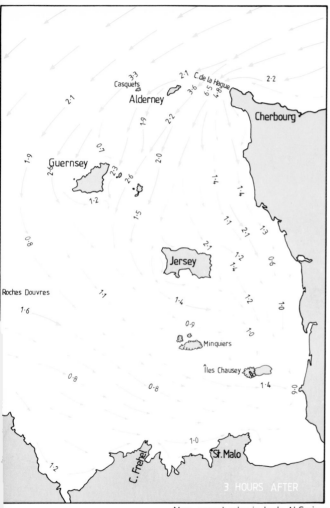

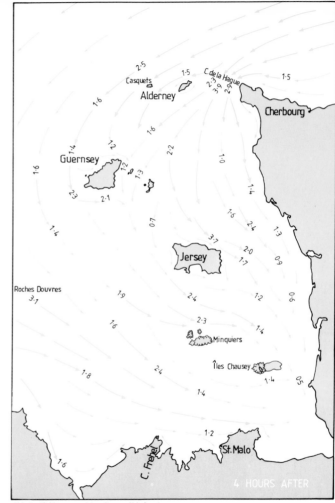

Mean current rates in knots. At Springs, add one-third. At Neaps, subtract one-third.

Mean current rates in knots. At Springs, add one-third. At Neaps, subtract one-third.

*22 OMONVILLE

Charts *Fr 5636 ; Im C33a ; (BA 1106 ; CG 528 ; Stan 16)*
High Water *—03h 40 Dover* *—00h 10 SP Cherbourg*
Heights above Datum *Springs MHW 6m2 MLW 1m1*
Neaps MHW 4m9 MLW 1m1

THE MAIN attraction in this peaceful little fishing harbour lies in its being only 6 miles from the Alderney Race and 8 miles west of Cherbourg. So long as the wind is settled between NNW and S it affords excellent shelter, but it is not a spot to be caught at if the wind should make up from an easterly quarter.

Approach From Cherbourg follow the coastline about a mile offshore until the village and breakwater lying on its N side appear. On rising ground above the waterfront cottages will be

22.1 Omonville at half-tide, showing why you should not attempt to lie alongside the seaward half of the breakwater. Front leading mark (A). Le Tunard beacon (B). Old Fort (C).

22.2   Yacht giving Le Tunard beacon a wide berth. Landing steps on the half-pier to the left.

seen the little chapel of Omonville-la-Rogue with its distinctive steeple. A W lattice pylon with a R top sited on the foreshore should be brought into line with the chapel on a course of 255° until bringing abeam to starboard the G beacon with triangular topmark on Le Tunard rocks about 1 cable ESE of the end of the breakwater. On the approach transit and to the west of Le Tunard beacon there is over 2m to within $\frac{3}{4}$ cable of the shore. At LW the rocks dry out.

By night the pylon shows an Iso WRG 4s. The narrow W sector has a range of 11 miles and brings the incoming yacht in along the approach described above. The R sector indicates being to the S of the correct approach. The G sector lies between N and 072° in the NE sector.

Coming from the N or W give a clear berth to the Basse Bréfort BY N-cardinal buoy lying 6 cables to the N of Pointe de Jardeheu and its signal station. The buoy has a VQ 10M all-round Lt. Hold on until Le Tunard beacon bears 195° (and you are well within the G sector of the shore Lt).

The leading transit is Le Tunard beacon in line with the old fort forming the SE extremity of the harbour. It has a small apart-ment building on it. A jink to port will be necessary to clear Le Tunard before swinging to starboard on to the approach transit from the E, as already described.

Berthing   The harbour dries out all along the breakwater and to a distance of $\frac{1}{2}$ cable elsewhere. There are several permanent French Navy mooring buoys.

Local fishermen use most of the inshore end of the alongside berths at the inshore end of the breakwater (dries 1m), which is the only part suitable for drying out alongside, or pick up a vacant mooring W of Le Tunard beacon and go ashore at the slip or steps at the little pier. Pic 22.1 shows how crowded it can be in summer. It also shows the extent of the rocky outcrop at the head of the harbour and alongside the outer half of the breakwater.

Facilities   Omonville's famous old cottage-restaurant is no longer, but there are shops and a new café of the kind more likely to appeal to day-trippers coming by land. Water available on the quay and the local garage will supply fuel. Beaumont-Hague 5km inland has a regular bus service to Cherbourg.

*23   ALDERNEY

Charts   *BA 60, 2845 ; Im C33a ; Fr 6934 ; (Stan 16)*
High Water   *−04h 10 Dover   +ooh 45 SP St Helier*
Heights above Datum   *Springs   MHW 6m3   MLW om8*
Neaps   MHW 4m7   MLW 2m6

ALDERNEY is only 60 miles from the Needles and no more than an overnight sail from any point of departure from Chichester or the West Country.

The island is less than 6 square miles, with a winter population of 2,000. Although only 8 miles due W of Cap de la Hague at the NW tip of the Cherbourg peninsula, it has owed allegiance to the English crown for over 900 years. The locals are friendly and easy-going, largely dependent on tourism and fishing for their livelihood. As with all the Channel Islands, taxes on booze and cigarettes are modest and the licensing hours dangerously flexible. There is no VAT. Also, there is no hurry.

Approach to landfall   The only harbour is Braye at the NE end of the island, situated at the bottom of a steep hill ½ mile from St Anne, the town. The harbour is open to NE'ly winds, when it is best avoided altogether.

23.1   Alderney lighthouse at the western end of the Race.

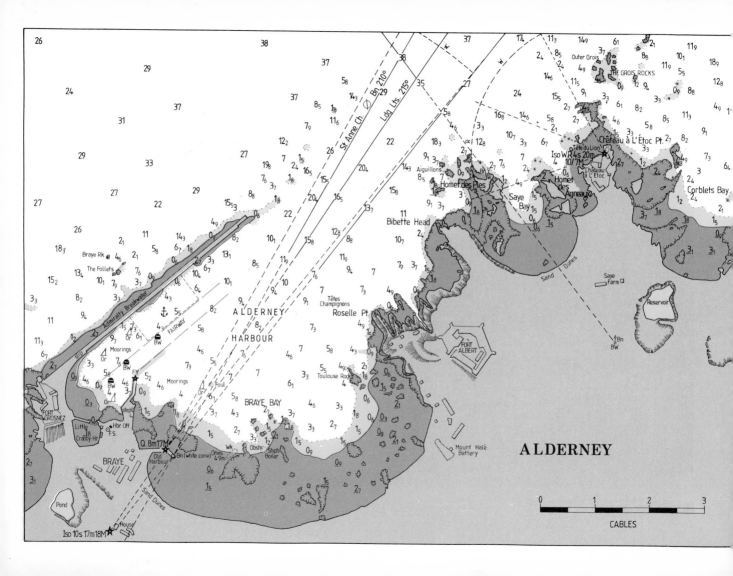

ALDERNEY

23.2   *Braye Harbour. Visitors' berths are moorings to the right of the fairway, which is clearly visible. Chateau à l'Étoc Point (A). Fort Albert (B). Old harbour breakwater light (C). St Anne town in background.*

The other factors which should be uppermost in one's mind when making a landfall:

(a) The Alderney Race runs up to 9 knots at springs. Slack water $\frac{1}{2}$h before HW Dover, after which it runs to the SW for the next $5\frac{1}{2}$h. It turns to the NE 6h before HW Dover and starts to slack off 5h later. Sailing from Cherbourg to Braye against a light westerly breeze in poor visibility I once held on to starboard tack for just a few minutes too long in a Class I ocean-racer and found myself shooting down the rapids in the direction of Quenard Point. Even with a powerful motor, normally good for 7 knots, we were unable to make the last mile to Braye, so had to give up lunch at the Divers and go south of the island—next stop the Scillies.

(b) Coming from the NW, if you first sight the Casquets (looking like a laden merchantman), consult the tidal atlas and decide then and there whether the last 8 miles to Braye harbour is best negotiated by standing well to the north of Burhou, or if the extra $3\frac{1}{2}$-miles passage S-about Alderney is not going to be quicker.

(c) Approaching from the S, if you miss the tide at the Race, make an early decision to head up for the Ortac channel between Burhou and the Casquets. In poor visibility under these circumstances it is best to go outside the Casquets altogether.

Navigational Aids

Radio The Aerobeacon situated in the middle of Alderney, callsign "ALD" on 383kHz, is continuous and has a range of 50 miles.

The Casquets Radio Beacon callsign "QS" on 298.8kHz is also a 50-mile signal. It is grouped with Start Point and Roches Douvres.

Cap Barfleur, callsign "FG" on 291.9kHz, is 35 miles E of Alderney, but its 70-mile signal is useful for fixing with either of the two beacons mentioned above.

The Channel LV, callsign "CR" on 287.3kHz, is a continuous beacon but has a range of only 10 miles. Situated 30 miles WNW

23.3 *Casquets lighthouse and surrounding danger.*

of Alderney it is only of interest to boats making a passage from the West Country.

Lights Cap de la Hague is Fl 5s from a 51m Grey tower. Its range is 23 miles and has a foghorn ev 30s. Long before seeing the loom of Cherbourg or even Cap de la Hague, the lights of the nuclear power station on the 180m skyline 3 miles SE of the lighthouse will appear, just as one sees the glow of the Fawley cracking-plant before sighting the Needles from the SW.

Alderney lighthouse is 1 mile E of the entrance to the harbour. It is Fl (4) 15s with a range of 28 miles. The fog siren is (4) 60s. The light is in a W round tower 32m high with a B band 37m above sea level.

Chateau à l'Étoc Point Lt is a W column ½ mile west of Alderney lighthouse. It is Iso WR 4s. Its W sector between 111° and 151° from seaward clears the end of the submerged breakwater. As it happens, the S edge of the W sector is in transit with Alderney lighthouse on 111°.

The Casquets is Fl (5) 30s 37m above sea level with 28 miles range. The tower is W, 23m high. There is a diaphone for signal (2) 60s.

Harbour Approach By day head for St Anne's church spire on 210°, which should be in transit with a W cone beacon on the end of the little breakwater of the Old Harbour. In practice simply middle the harbour entrance, keeping well inside the shoal water which extends 3 cables NE of the seaward end of the Admiralty breakwater. It has a least depth of 1m2, but there can be overfalls in the vicinity.

By night bring into transit the Q W Lt 17m range with the Iso W 10s rear Lt, range 18M. These lights show over 10° sectors either side of the 215° transit course.

Berthing Yachts must either anchor where they can or pick up one of the eighty yellow conical visitors' mooring-buoys close to the breakwater. Under no circumstances can boats go alongside the breakwater or jetty, which is reserved for commercial craft including the hydrofoil from Guernsey. Anchor either side of the fairway as shown on the chart.

VHF watch is maintained on Ch16 and 12 from 0800 to 1800. The Harbour Officer who doubles as Customs Officer, is to be found between these hours at the office at the inshore end of the jetty, tel. (048–182) 2620.

There are no plans for pontoon berths (1984).

Facilities Water is available at the berthing quay near the HO, where prior arrangements should be made.

Diesel and chandlery is available at Mainbrayce Ltd in the Inner Harbour, petrol and calor gas from Alderney Stores & Bunkering Co (the Sail Loft), Braye Street.

Alderney Sailing Club is next to the HO.

Showers, heads and laundromats on the Commercial Quay.

Boat repairs are available near the harbour.

Landing on the Admiralty Breakwater or slip is forbidden.

Land either at the steps at the inshore end of the jetty or at the Sapper slip just below the Sailing Club.

Excellent shopping and a wide choice of restaurants in St Anne.

Airline direct flights to the other Channel Islands, Southampton, Bournemouth and Cherbourg.

Weather reports on BBC Radio 4 200kHz. Area Portland.

Charts   *Fr 827 ; Im C33a ; (BA 3655)*
High Water   *−04h 33 Dover   +0h 05 SP St Helier*
Heights above Datum   *Springs   MHW 11m2 MLW 1m4*
  Neaps   MHW 7m9 MLW 4m0

LYING 13 miles NE of Jersey and 22 miles S of Cap de la Hague, Carteret with Barneville, its twin town on the opposite side of the R. Gerfleur estuary, is more of interest for its beaches, excellent restaurants and hotels than as a port for visiting yachtsmen. However, it is recommended as a possible day excursion from Gorey on the east coast of Jersey in high-speed ferries whose timetables are dictated by the tides and need to be checked (for example, some of the departures are at 0500). For a boat prepared to take the ground and stop over through LW it is straightforward to enter or leave any time within an hour of HW.

Approach   Cap de Carteret immediately N of the harbour entrance has a prominent lighthouse with a Grey square tower 15m high on top of the cliff. The light is 81m above sea level and shows a 26-mile range Fl (2+1) 15s and a horn (3) ev 60s. Shoal water of less than 2m will be encountered 0.9 miles south of the harbour entrance at springs. In violent W'ly winds there may be a big sea breaking over the bar ½ mile outside the entrance, which dries 3m3 at LWS. The precise depth and position of the bar tends to move. The tidal currents running parallel to the coastline attain 4 knots at springs, but are nearly slack during the last hour before HW.

The western breakwater 500m long lies N–S with a R-topped W Lt beacon at its extremity (Oc R 4s 6m 7 miles range). A mole

24.1   Near HW Carteret looks attractive, with the channel clearly defined. (A) is the 'Gare Maritime'. (B) the main hotel and slipway. (C) Port de Refuge. (D) the 'Marina' soi-disant.

24.2   *Gare Maritime with Jersey ferry alongside and south bank mole exposed.*

24.3   *View of harbour at low water from public slip.*

24.4 *The 'Marina' at low water. Compare with picture 24.1.*

on the eastern side of the entrance is considerably shorter than the breakwater. It is submerged at the upper end of each tide, but has a G unlit beacon at its southern extremity, which always shows.

There is a prominent W hotel on the riverside. The G beacon should be brought into transit with the left-hand edge of the hotel on a course of 010°. Give the R-topped Lt beacon on the western breakwater a fair berth, as it has shoal water close alongside. Once inside, favour the left bank, keeping close to it all the way.

Berthing

1   The first and best berth alongside the wall is reserved for the ferries (pic 24.2 shows one dried out) alongside the pretentiously-named Gare Maritime, a wooden shack with Customs and the HO near by.

2   If not fully occupied by fishing boats a drying berth along-side the quay S of the R beacon with can topmark may be sought, but between this beacon and the slip outside the two big hotels (Marine and Angleterre) there are stone groynes.

3   Immediately upstream of the hotels is a small cut (Port de Refuge) where one can dry out alongside.

Beyond that one comes to the 'marina', a collection of mud berths. But, be warned, the stench of the mud and slime at LW is overpowering.

Facilities   Besides the hotels and excellent restaurants (one of which rates two crossed forks in the Michelin Guide) there are a yacht chandlery, garages with yacht mechanics, FW and provision stores. The small YC (CN Carteret-Barneville) has a sailing school. Weather is posted there. Area 11 Manche ouest.

The port authority's tel. is (33) 54–88–72.

25 GUERNSEY

Charts *BA 807, 808, 3140 ; Fr 6903 ; Im 33a ; Stan 16 ; (CG 014)*
High Water *−04h 50 Dover* *+00h 10 SP St Helier*
Heights above Datum *Springs* *MHW 9m0 MLW 1m0*
                      Neaps *MHW 6m7 MLW 3m5*

ᏀUERNSEY, at 27 square miles, is the second largest of the Channel Islands, 9 miles long and just 4½ across at its widest point. ᛏt is the seat of government of the ancient Bailiwick of Guernsey, ᴡhich includes Alderney, Sark, Herm and Jethou. Its resident ᴩopulation of 55,000, to which each year are added 400,000 tourᴤts attracted by tax-free shopping, superb sandy beaches and catering trade geared to the needs of visitors accustomed to ᴍore restricted or expensive facilities.

About 10,000 yachts touch down in Guernsey each year, hence ᴛhe edict that visiting boats cannot stay beyond 14 days without ᴩecial permission from the HM. One of Guernsey's special ᴛtractions to visitors in their own boats is the wide variety of ᴅay-trips which can be made to quiet anchorages on the four ᴍaller islands lying within six miles of St Peter Port. Creux harᴅour on the east coast of Sark is the most attractive and has 1m4 ᴡater at LWN. Local ferries also ply between them and claim ᴩriority alongside the available berths at Herm or Sark. It is thus ᴩreferable to anchor off.

ᏚT PETER PORT The only town on Guernsey is also the one ᴤheltered harbour accessible at any state of the tide (pic ᴤ5.1). It is 65 miles from Weymouth, 82 from the Needles and ᴤ5 from Plymouth. From a distance the island looks like a steep-ᴅ plateau (90m maximum) which it is along the South coast.

On a sunny day the landfall may be announced by the sun flashing off the greenhouses (tomatoes and flowers) long before the low-lying beaches of the NW coast are seen.

Approach There is an Aerobeacon emitting continuously on 361kHz callsign "GUR" with a range of 30 miles, but it is located near the SW extremity of the island.

From the Alderney Race The most direct route is through the *Little Russel Channel* just 4 miles from St Peter Port, but unmarked rocks lie in wait 2 miles NE of the entrance to the channel. Whereas the tidal streams run along the grain of the channel, up to 5 knots at springs, it has marked E–W components across one's track not very far to seaward. The tide starts to ebb to the SW 1½h before HW Dover and will be flooding to the NE 6h later, or 4½h after HW Dover.

Assuming tide and visibility permit an approach through the Little Russel, the first Lt to be picked up will be Platte Fougère (Fl WR 10s 15m 16M). Its R sector 085°–155° covers the unmarked Braye rocks which extend 1 mile to the NW. Its tower is W, with a B base and broad B band half-way up. It has a Racon beacon, callsign "P".

The eastern side of the channel is first marked by the BW beacon on Tautenay rocks, one mile due north of Herm. Its light is Q (3) WR 6s 7m high and 7M range. The R sector (215°–050°) warns of outlying dangers to the E and S.

Right in the middle of the channel is the BW chequered stone tower 8m high on Roustel shoal (pic 25.2). Its Q 7M Lt should be brought in line on course 198° with an Iso 4s Lt 9-miles range on top of the 19m high flat fort on Brehon island (pic 25.3).

The alternative transit is 208° aligning Brehon with the 14M light on St Martin's Point 2 miles S of St Peter Port. It is Fl (3) WR 10s, a 9m flat building 15m above the sea. Its R sector only applies if cutting the corner too fine from the SW.

Brehon should be left to port. The harbour leading lights on 220° bring into transit: St Peter Port Castle breakwater (Alt WR

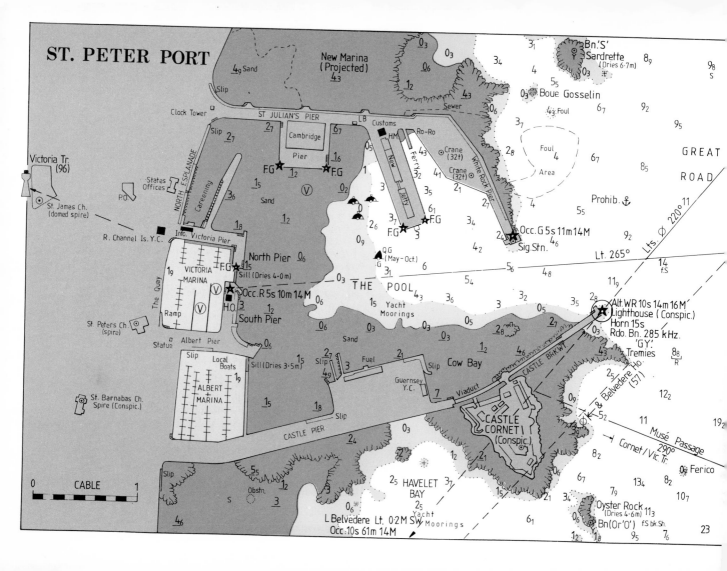

25.1   *St Peter Port with Herm and Jethou beyond. (A) open anchorage Havelet bay. (B) Castle Cornet. (C) commercial berths. (D) Afloat moorings for visitors. (E) Albert Marina (locals). (F) Victoria Marina (some visitors). (G) Harbour Office and Customs.*

145

10s 14m 16M)—pic 25.4—and Belvedere (Oc 10s 61m 14M), a small W tower with an Or stripe, perched on the cliff beyond Castle Cornet and also nearly in transit with twin radio masts, each with FR lights.

Between Roustel and Brehon the Platte Lt is left to starboard. It should not be confused with Platte Fougère mentioned above. It is 7 cables ENE of the entrance to St Sampson. Its Lt is Fl WR 3s 6m and 5M. The structure is a G conical stone tower.

A local Radio Beacon at the end of the southern breakwater transmits continuously on 285kHz, callsign "GY", but its range is only 10 miles. The foghorn ev 15s from the same point may be useful. It is synchronised with the Radio Beacon. It makes its callsign "GY" four times and then emits a steady note for 27s. The horn sounds off at the start of the steady radio transmission. The number of seconds from the start of the dash until the horn is heard times 1.8 is the distance off in cables.

The breakwater head to starboard—White Rock Pier—has a 14M Oc G 5s light on the signal station 11m above the water.

A FR light at the pierheads prohibits entry or exit, except for small boats under power who keep well clear of big ship movements.

The Big Russel Channel between Herm and Sark is much easier if there are doubts about tides or visibility. It is 3 miles wide with some off-lying dangers stretching 1 mile SSW of Jethou. If in doubt head SW to leave the Lower Heads S-cardinal buoy to starboard. Its light is Q (6) + LFl 10s. From there to the harbour entrance is a little over 2 miles on course made good of 305°. From Alderney it is only 2 miles farther than going through the Little Russel.

There are various short cuts, of which the Musé Passage is the simplest: by day this lines up the right-hand edge of Castle Cornet with the castellated Victoria Tower (96m) on 291°.

From St Malo or Jersey the approach is simple. Just head for St Martin's Point (see above) and leave it to port.

25.2 *Roustel shoal beacon.*

25.3 *Brehon tower.*

25.4   St Peter Port Castle breakwater light with Castle Cornet.

From the N or W it is easiest to approach St Peter Port S-about the island, giving the awesome Les Hanois Lighthouse a wide berth, because unmarked rocks extend some distance to seaward. This is particularly so if coming down from the Casquets (as in the RORC race from Cowes) where dangers lurk 2 miles off the NW shore of Guernsey. The lighthouse is Grey, 36m high. Its light is Q (2) 5s with a range of 23 miles. It has a horn (2) 60s. The Aerobeacon "GUY" is 2 miles due E of Les Hanois. The tide off the corner turns about the same time as in the Little Russel. Close along the S coast it runs mostly E–W.

Berthing in St Peter Port   St Peter Port radio keeps watch on Ch16 VHF with Ch78 and 12 (Port Control) as working frequencies.

At the harbour entrance Port Control will direct visiting yachts to their berths. That may be on the Y buoys W of the New Pier or on visitors' pontoons on the southern half of Victoria Marina, tel. (0481) 25987 (pic 25.6).

Entrance to the marina is only possible 3h either side of HW. There is a depth of 1m9 maintained in Victoria Marina. Tide gauges indicate the water over the sill. There is a waiting pontoon outside the sill if the tide is not suitable, but it dries at LW.

A Customs/Immigration form must be completed within 2h of arrival. The HO and Customs Office are both on the jetty of St Julian's Pier, which protects the harbour from the N. Tel. (0481) 20029.

Most of the moorings which remain afloat at all tides and the Albert Marina berths are reserved for local owners. All the along-side berths outside the marinas are for commercial traffic only.

There is a speed limit of 4 knots in the harbour, which also applies to yacht tenders. Batteries may not be charged after noon.

CHANNEL ISLANDS YACHT MARINA, VALE (pic 25.8)   On the NE extremity of Guernsey there used to be a flooded quarry at Beaucette. They dynamited a cut, thus letting

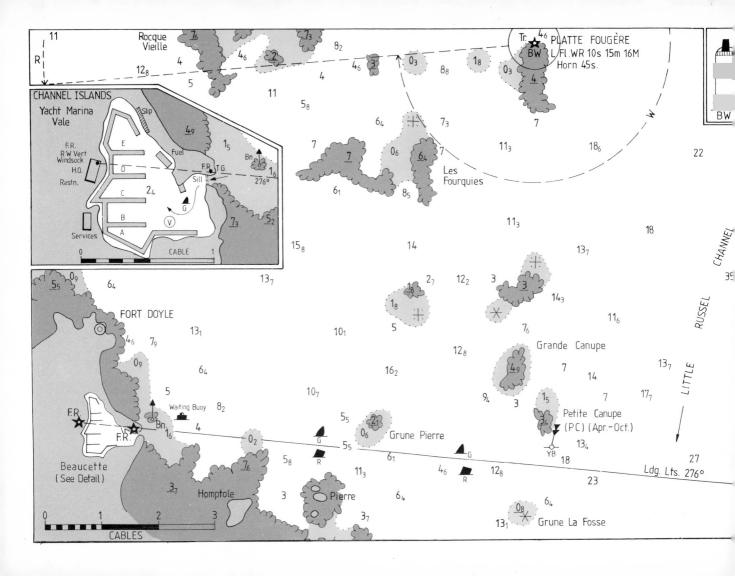

25.5   *Les Hanois from WSW. Note off-lying danger.*

25.6   Looking over the sill at Victoria Marina. Visitors' berths on right of picture.

25.7   The careening harbour next to Victoria Marina.

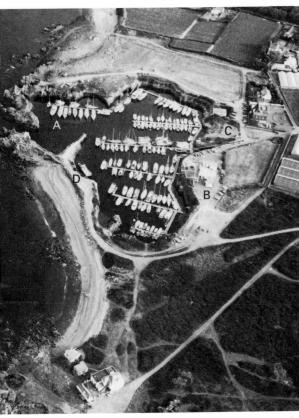

5.8 *Beaucette Channel Islands Yacht Marina at Vale. Visitors' berths (A). Harbour Office and clubhouse (B). Site of new services under construction (1983) (C). Fuel point (D).*

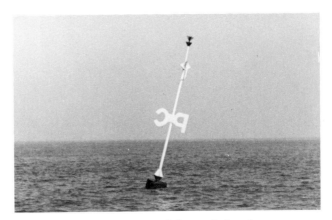

25.9 *Petite Canupe buoy at east end of approach channel.*

in the sea creating a 200-berth marina in perfect shelter. The approach channel is from the Little Russel, about half-way between Platte Fougère and Roustel beacons. The entrance is not easy to spot even from a mile off. So look for Fort Doyle on the right-hand edge of land. The marina is 2 cables S of that point.

Some 7 cables due E of the entrance is the unlit S-cardinal buoy marking the Petite Canupe rocks. This YB spar buoy has the letters PC on it (pic 25.9). Leaving it close to starboard, head inshore on course 277°. In the summer the channel is marked by two pairs of small R and G fairway buoys.

The leading marks are: Front—A wide vertical R line and pole over a W background on the N head of the entrance; Rear—a mast on the white clubhouse building has a W board with a R vertical stripe on it. There is also a windsock on the same mast.

25.10 *The entrance is only 18 metres wide. Note tide gauge and leading marks. The rear one is normally shown on the flagpole with windsock at the right-hand edge of the white building.*

(In pic 25.10 this board is temporarily down for repainting.) There are FR Lts on both leading marks.

To avoid hitting the N side of the entrance or the rock with a beacon just outside, it is necessary to make a late jink to port to pass through the entrance and leave to starboard the 'breakwater' made of old tractor tyres. Pic 25.10 shows the very prominent tide gauge giving the level over the sill. It has 2m7 over it at half-tide and there's 18m0 in the basin at all times. Entry can always be made ± 3h on HW, sometimes for longer. There is negligible cross-current just off the entrance.

Listening watch is kept on VHF Ch16 and on M band 157.85kHz.

Visitors berths are just inside the entrance on the S side. Fuel, FW, provisions and chandlery are all available.

The HO is on the top deck above the restaurant, which is excellent. Telephone numbers: Harbour Administration (0481) 45000 and 47071; Restaurant 47066.

The only snag about this marina is that it is a long taxi-ride to St Peter Port and even farther to the airport, but, as mentioned above, there is no need to leave the marina area at all during a

25.11 Restaurant and clubhouse.

25.12 Entrance looking to seaward. Visitors' berths unusually empty, even for mid winter.

short visit. L'Ancresse Bay is generally reckoned to be the finest bathing beach on the island. It is within walking distance.

ST SAMPSON Between Beaucette and St Peter Port is the harbour of St Sampson, which dries out beyond its entrance. It has a dockyard and too many other manifestations of its commercial character to be of interest to visiting yachtsmen, but some boats have winter berths there, and it is the only place where major repairs can be carried out. The HM keeps watch on Ch16.

From a point equidistant between Platte and Brehon lights, the leading marks on course 286° are: the post on the S pierhead (Lt FR 3m 5M) in line with the 12m-high clocktower on the S side, close to the entrance of the inner harbour.

Guernsey Facilities St Peter Port has everything to be expected in a thriving tourist resort and financial community. The Royal Channel Islands YC is on the front right opposite the NW corner of Victoria Marina. Guernsey YC is half-way along Castle Pier.

There is an efficient information office on Victoria Pier.

Communications: by air and/or sea to the other Channel Islands, St Malo, Weymouth, Portsmouth and London.

26 JERSEY

Charts *BA 1137, 3728; Im 33b; Stan 16; Fr 5232; (CG 1014)*
High Water *−04h 33 Dover +00h 05 SP St Helier*
Heights above Datum *Springs MHW 11m1 MLW 1m3*
                        Neaps MHW 8m1 MLW 4m1

JERSEY is the largest and most prosperous of all the Channel Islands. It is 10 miles E–W and only 5½ miles across at its widest point. There are 77,000 inhabitants, swollen by about 800,000 visitors a year. Besides servicing the tourists, the principal industry on the island is making money. A stroll downtown brings one face-to-face with many of the familiar brass plates to be found outside offices in the City of London, but it is also redolent of history from William the Conqueror's day to the Nazi occupation in 1940–5.

This is the nearest British territory to France, just 12 miles W of the Cherbourg peninsula, 22 from the Île de Chausey and 36 from St Malo.

With its huge rise and fall of tide, nearly 10m at springs, it was never a popular place for visiting English yachts, unless they were prepared to dry out, row miles ashore in a dinghy or suffer my experience alongside in St Helier. We went ashore for dinner

26.1   La Corbière lighthouse from the north-west. Give it a wide berth. Note causeway joining land.

ST. HELIER

From BA chart 3278.

CABLES

26.2 Noirmont Point from the west.

leaving our bulwarks level with the quayside. Returning three hours later we had to get back on board by way of the upper spreaders. Now it's all changed, with a magnificent new 450-berth marina in the heart of town.

Approach to St Helier   Although entry over the sill to the new marina is ±3h on HW and sometimes better, access to La Colette Yacht Basin immediately outside the main harbour entrance is at all states of the tide; there is a waiting pontoon (D) for boats who have time to kill. On passage to St Helier from any direction it is therefore easier if the ETA can be adjusted to the top half of the tide.

Consider first a passage from the north   Around La Corbière Lt at the SW corner of the island (pic 26.1) the tide turns southerly 3h after HW Dover ($-4\frac{1}{2}$h on HW St Helier) and runs strongly to the E along the S coast until 5h before HW Dover (or HW St Helier). That suits very well, since one could make the 35 miles from Alderney Race or any intermediate point on the same tide. Like Les Hanois, La Corbière lighthouse has shoal water with breaking seas up to 7 cables to the WNW over Green Rock. But it is an 18-mile Lt Iso WR 10s from a 19m W stone tower 36m above sea level (pic 26.1). Its foghorn sounds C ev

60s. Its R sectors warn those who are either cutting it a bit fine around Grosnez Point or taking a chance to the SE of the buoyed channel past St Brelade's Bay. It has a Radio Beacon callsign "CB" on 305.7kHz with a 20-mile range.

A safe check on one's approach course from the N is the W-cardinal buoy (Q (9) 15s) marking the Banc Desormes 4 miles NW of Grosnez. There is plenty of water to pass either side of it, provided that by day you keep La Corbière open of the right-hand edge of Jersey on 177°; or by night you stay in the W sector of Grosnez light (Fl (2) WR 15s 50m 19M). There is also a continuous Aerobeacon at the end of the runway over St Ouen Bay: callsign "JW" on 329kHz.

Past Corbière you run parallel to the shore about $\frac{1}{2}$ mile offshore for 3 miles so as to pass close to seaward of the BW hooped tower on Noirmont Point 18m above the water (pic 26.2). It is a 13-mile Lt Fl (4) 12s. The Western Passage for deep-draught ships passes between Noirmont and a N-cardinal buoy with Q Lt 3 cables outside on course 082°.

By night this is easy, with two shore Lts in transit (Oc 5s 14M and Alt WR 14M). By day their R bar on a W tower and another W tower are not so easy to pick out, except that they are near some high-rise buildings on the SE corner of the island. Still on 082°, $1\frac{1}{2}$ miles after Noirmont, you should pick up the W pillar-and-globe beacon on the Dog's Nest rocks and, 2 cables short of it, the Q G conical buoy marking East Rock.

Here you alter 60° to port on to the R and G passage (023°) for 7 cables to the harbour entrance—so called because the front leading light is Oc G 5s 8m 11M on a W daymark, while the rear Lt is Oc R 5s 20m 12M on a R structure (pic 26.3).

On the way in you leave close to port the Platte Rock R lattice beacon (Fl R 1.5s) which has just been re-erected after an incoming ferry nudged it in 1983.

From the S, W-about the Minquiers   You can head for Passage Rock N-cardinal buoy (VQ) off St Brelade's Bay 125°—2 miles

26.3 *St Helier seen on Red and Green transit 023°. (A) Platte Rock beacon. (B) Fuel berth. (C) La Colette yacht harbour. (D) Jersey Marina. (E) Old harbour. (F) Land being reclaimed.*

26.4   La Colette yacht harbour with New Harbour (commercial) to the left and oil terminal on the right.

from Corbière light—and then follow the Western Passage as described above leaving to starboard the channel buoys heading for the Dog's Nest; or keeping 2 miles offshore, head towards the Demie de Pas light tower 1½ miles SSE of St Helier (YB tower, Lt Mo D WR 12s 11m 14M with foghorn (3) 60s). About 1½ miles short you pick up the R and G passage described above and head for the harbour on 023°.

From the E, or E-about the Minquiers Aim to leave the Demie de Pas (see above) to starboard and make good a course 341° along the S Passage, heading towards a BW mark bearing 341° on the shore of St Aubin's Bay, being sure to leave the R can Hinguette buoy to port (Fl (4) R 15s). Just short of the E Rock buoy, alter to 023° on the R and G Passage described above.

It is all straightforward provided you remember that the tidal currents run EW up to 3½ knots at springs and 1½ knots at neaps.

Berthing in St Helier Traffic is controlled from the signal tower at the head of Victoria pier. The fact that you pass two other harbour entrances on your starboard hand before you get there should not disturb you. The first is the tanker berth; the second is the entrance to La Colette Yacht Basin, increasingly being adopted by the fishing fleet.

Traffic control: listen out on VHF Ch14. The Lt signals are simple:

G: vessels may enter, but not leave

R: cleared to leave but not enter

R and G: no movement permitted. An exception to this is a Q Amber Lt which allows boats of less than 25m LOA to enter or leave under power against the signals above. In doing so, keep to starboard of the fairway.

The speed limit is 5 knots. No battery charging after noon.

Entrance to the marina is normally ± 3h on HW. A tide gauge shows the water over the sill, and R or G lights control movement. If you draw over 1m8 you should inform Port Control so as to be allocated a suitable berth. Inside the marina visiting

26.5 *Jersey yacht club and fuel point. Tide gauges alongside steps show it to be at the bottom of low water springs.*

26.6 *Old Harbour with boats in cradles.*

26.7 *Sill and gate leading into Jersey Marina. Note traffic lights and tide gauge on right-hand side. Fort Regent on skyline.*

town St Helier you can go on to a holding berth in La Colette, but it is not as well protected from the swell as the chart might suggest, and the facilities ashore are limited. There are Q R and G fairway buoys at the entrance. Be sure to leave the R can buoy to port on turning to starboard to enter. It looks all wrong, but there is a long list of groundings by yachts who have left it the wrong side.

Fuel is only available outside the marina on the S pier by the St Helier YC opposite the harbour entrance. You need half-tide to go alongside. All other facilities are available on the dockside of the marina.

Other Harbours and their Approaches The only other harbour which allows a boat to lie afloat at all states of the tide is St Catherine at the NE extremity of the island. It is a single breakwater, wide open between E and SSE and you have to anchor off. Once ashore there are only very sketchy amenities. However, it can be approached from the NW down Le Ruan Channel between Jersey or the Paternosters and Les Écrehou. This channel is deep and 3 miles wide, but not recommended in poor visibility. There is no light of any significance until you pick up the Fl 1.5s at the end of the St Catherine breakwater. It has a range of 13M. Final approach should always be made from due E or somewhat N of it. Tuck close under the end of the breakwater and anchor in 3m5 about a cable offshore.

Farther S by 1½ miles from St Catherine is *Gorey*, the picture postcard little port under the lee of the floodlit Mont Orgueil Castle, with plenty to commend it ashore by way of hostelries and sight-seeing. It is the home port of the vedettes which ply between there and Carteret on a bizarre timetable dictated by the tides. If you fancy a day-trip with an 0500 departure, it's worth it. Customs can be cleared here.

The harbour all but dries out and is very crowded in the summer. The only afloat berths are those alongside the outer end of the pier, and they are usually taken up by ferries or fishing

yachts normally go to F or G pontoons, the farthest from the entrance, although boats over 12.5m LOA or 2m draft may be accommodated on A pontoon. The Marina Office is tel. (0534) 79549. Stays of more than two weeks' duration must be cleared with the HM. The weather is posted there.

If you arrive before half-tide or want to be away from down-

26.8   Gorey : 298° leading transit of church steeple (A) and breakwater end shown.

boats. There is a local HO to appeal to, but, unless you are prepared to dry out some distance up-harbour, it is not too attractive.

Approaching from any direction keep ½ mile to seaward until the leading marks are picked up on 298°. They are: the light tower at the end of Gorey pier in line with Gorey church steeple. There are lights, but it would be lunacy for a visitor to attempt entry at night, not knowing whether there is even an anchor berth available.

Passage from S-about the island is by way of the Vi Channel, which is an A-level examination for coastal navigators. Provided you find the W-cardinal Canger Rock buoy (Q (9) 15s) 3 miles SSE of La Rocque Point and leave it close to starboard on a course made good of 075° it is worth a go. If the visibility is less

26.9　Gorey harbour on top half of tide. See slipway at head of the harbour and Mont Orgueil Castle.

than 5 miles, forget it—unless you have a local pilot. There is a RWVS spar buoy Fl 10s 2 miles beyond Canger Rock buoy. Here course should be altered to port to put the unlit beacon on Petite Anquette 1 mile away broad on the starboard bow. You must then pick up the 332° leading line of Verclut Point (at the inshore end of St Catherine breakwater) and turret on Coupe Point (right-hand edge of land) just ½ mile beyond it. From this point it is a little over 3 miles to pick up the Gorey Harbour

transit. First you should leave to port the unlit R can buoy marking Le Giffard Rock, 2 miles from the Vi Channel.

The other and even more attractive harbour is *St Aubin* just 2 miles W of St Helier across the bay. It is the home of the well-appointed and very hospitable Royal Channel Islands YC (Jersey). But it dries out to a distance of ½ mile from the entrance, well beyond the historic St Aubin Fort (pic 26.12) where some dinghy sailors keep their boats hauled out. The small harbour

26.10   *St Aubin looks inviting at the top of the tide.*

26.11   Harbour entrance. Men in work-boat are trying to disperse mud with chemicals.

26.12   Fort St Aubin at low water.

26.13   Typical harbour scene at low water. Note south breakwater is kept clear for crane operation.

is packed out, so there is no point in going there except to anchor off for the top half of a tide or by prior arrangement.

If determined to do so, the safest course is to head inshore at Diamond Rock R can buoy (Fl (2) R 6s), a port-hand buoy on the Western Passage just under 1 mile E of Noirmont Point and a similar distance W of the Dog's Nest. Here you head for the Martello Tower on the shore NE of St Aubin Harbour on course 345°, leaving well open on your port bow the Grosse Rocks Beacon and the Castle. As soon as you have a clear sight of the harbour entrance, head towards it on course 252°. The fairway is marked by small R and G buoys. If you must approach by night, the N pierhead has a 12m metal Lt tower with a 10-mile

26.14   Royal Channel Islands yacht club at St Aubin.

Lt Iso R 4s. There is also a WRG directional Lt with $\pm 1°$ W Lt on course, a 5° G sector if off course to starboard and a corresponding R sector 5° to south of the W sector.

There is no resident HM at St Aubin, so visiting yachts must take pot luck in a free-for-all. Securing alongside the S breakwater is prohibited because it is where the crane operates. You might be lucky and find a drying berth on very soft mud against the east breakwater.

Facilities at Jersey   The island has sub-tropical vegetation, many luxurious homes, several hotels of the very highest class, restaurants to satisfy the most fastidious, bars and bistros for all tastes and wonderful tax-free shopping.

It is also famous for its new all-purpose leisure and conference centre built within Fort Regent overlooking St Helier, with access by cable car. In the country there is the underground hospital just as the Nazis left it in 1945 and, near by, Gerald Durrell's world-famous zoo. La Moye golf course near the SW tip of the island is of international standard. There's surfing, board-sailing, horse racing and much pageantry and junketing.

Every kind of chandlery and yacht repairs can be undertaken.

The Tourist Information Office is next to the HM's at the town end of the marina (if you survive crossing the road there). The HM is tel. (0534) 34451.

St Helier is linked by sea to the other Channel Islands, Carteret, Granville and St Malo on the French coast and to Weymouth and Portsmouth by regular ferry.

Occasional sea mist and crosswinds permitting, there are flights to Southampton, London, Paris, Guernsey and Cherbourg, while charter aircraft come in from all over Europe.

Charts *Fr 829, 830 ; CG 535 ; (BA 3659 ; Im C 33b)*
High Water *—05h 00 Dover —00h 15 SP St Helier*
Heights above Datum *Springs MHW 12m9 MLW 1m9*
  Neaps MHW 9m8 MLW 4m9

THE ÎLES CHAUSEY are a formidable collection of rocks and reefs spread over an area 6½ miles E–W and 2 miles across which emerge at LW after a fall of as much as 11m to look like the surface of the moon.

The only inhabited island is La Grande Île, where about 100 residents go fishing or make the most of the day-trippers who swarm over the place in the summer after making the 10-mile crossing from Granville or 15 miles from St Malo in vedettes. If you go aground you are apt to suffer the indignity of having cows grazing round your boat at LW.

All the action—by which I mean a general store, two bistros and the landing points—are at the SE end of Grande Île. Here also is the narrow deep-water channel where afloat berths or moorings can be found even at LW springs.

All the charts make it look more difficult than it really is, if one does not get too ambitious in attempting any of the entrance channels except that close SE of the only lighthouse (pic 27.2).

Approach From anywhere but the N, there is deep water up to the SE point of Grand Île, where the most prominent feature is the 19m Grey square tower of the lighthouse, standing 40m above sea level (pic 27). Its Lt is Fl 5s with a range of 23M. Hold off about ½ mile until the 3 E-cardinal beacons leading out from the point can be left clear to port on the approach course of 332°. This will put ahead La Crabière Est, a conspicuous B tripod structure with Y top on a rock off the slipway, which is

used as a landing point on the top half of the tide. It has an Oc WRG 4s Lt. Its W sector 3° either side of 332° is in transit with an unlit W tower B top, L'Enseigne, 1¼ miles beyond Crabière tripod, but none the less easily picked out.

Of more immediate interest is the G conical buoy marking Les Epiettes with a Lt Fl G 2s on it. Leaving this buoy to starboard it is prudent to 'borrow' a little to the E of the transit especially at LW where there is shoal water across the channel from the W. At the S-cardinal beacon, to be left to starboard, one is in the pool of relatively deep water which continues along the well-marked channel for a further ½ mile.

Approach from the North Those with local knowledge find the dog-leg Grande Entrée approach from the NW along unlit transits through the rocks simple enough. But coming from St Helier it saves only 1½ miles against using the deep-water channel Entrée de la Deroute W-about Chausey. It is recommended that this course should be adopted at least until one has had the experience of sailing out to sea through the Grande Entrée from Grande Île anchorage.

The rocks extend 2½ miles to the NW and W of Grande Île with only one beacon to mark their limit (La Concalaise in the WSW).

The Entrée de la Deroute channel is marked by the E-cardinal Les Ardentes pillar buoy (Q (3) 10s) 3.7 miles SE of the NE Minquiers buoy. After steering SW for 3½ miles from rounding Les Ardentes in the W sector of La Crabière Lt (see above), follow the line of the Chausey outcrops round to the S and SE until picking up the normal approach described above.

Tidal streams of up to 3½ knots run southward past the western side of Chausey from 2½h before HW St Helier (2½h before HW Dover), turning northward 3h after HW St Helier (4¼h after HW Dover). Close to the N or S of the islands the E-going stream starts 6h before HW St Helier (+1½h Dover); the tides run W ¼h before HW St Helier and 5¼h before HW Dover.

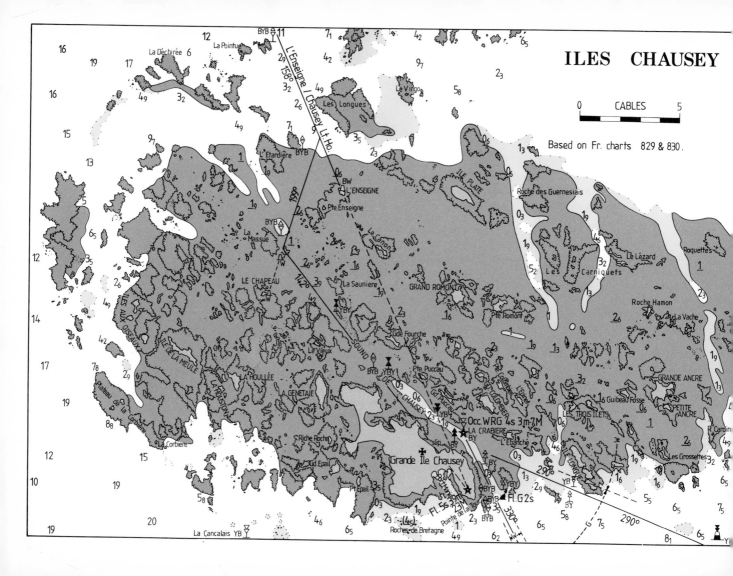

ILES CHAUSEY

Based on Fr. charts 829 & 830.

CABLES 0 ——— 5

27.1 *Approaching from the south, boats can be seen at anchor in most of the deepwater part of the Sound. The lighthouse is on the nearest point. Landing slip and jetty are the other side of the hill.*

27.2   Lighthouse from a cable off to south-east.

27.3   Three east-cardinal beacons to be left to port on final approach.

27.4   La Crabière Est tripod with Oc light. Deepest water is found immediately south-east of this light.

Inside the anchorage off Grande Île the tide is not so fierce, somewhat under 3 knots. It runs to the NW for 9h from 5½h before HW St Helier (2h after HW Dover). The reverse stream only runs for 3½h at most.

Departure through NW channel—Grande Entrée Leaving the anchorage on 310° proceed to the pair of W- and E-cardinal beacons close off the northern tip of Grande Île. Through there on course 325° for 9 cables you should be heading for the W-cardinal Grunes de la Massue beacon with the W chimney beacon marking La Massue fine on the port bow.

Another W chimney beacon will be seen wide on the port beam (Le Chapeau). Coming up to Grunes de la Massue beacon, alter 5 points to starboard to 020° bringing the two W chimney beacons on to a stern transit. Half a mile on, this course will bring a W-cardinal buoy abeam and take you on to the reverse transit of L'Enseigne W tower (B top) with the main Grande Île lighthouse on course 335° for the open sea. After taking this departure course for ½ mile there is a W-cardinal beacon to be left clear to port. At this point the echo sounder should give a sudden and clear indication that you have broken clear of the archipelago formed, it is said, by a cataclysmic event thirteen centuries ago.

There are several other well-attested channels through the rocks, some of them leading into the Sound, but these are outside the scope of this book.

Berthing and Facilities Finding a suitable spot to anchor in the Sound, especially during July and August, is a matter of luck. There are several mooring buoys which may be available. For example, the YC Granville have some of their own. So have the vedettes, who rarely stop overnight, which opens the possibility of picking one up. My solution is to ring the landlord at the Hôtel du Fort to book a table, when he may have a constructive suggestion.

Whatever happens you will not be allowed to lie alongside either the jetty used by the vedettes at low tides or the slipway for HW use. Wherever you leave your dinghy, look ahead to the height the tide is likely to have reached when you return. Many have found their dinghy afloat but its painter secured out of reach underwater.

Apart from the hospitality of the two bistros, the local store offers limited provisioning.

There are no customs or police at Chausey, so in theory you should have officially entered France first, but they are well accustomed to visiting yachts from St Helier. Weather Area 11 Manche ouest.

*28 GRANVILLE

Charts   *Fr 5897 ; Im 33b ; Stan 16*
High Water   −05h 10 Dover   −00h 15 SP St Helier
Heights above Datum   *Springs*   *MHW 12m8 MLW 1m4*
          Neaps   *MHW 9m6 MLW 4m6*

GRANVILLE is an old walled city of 16,000 inhabitants built on a high (50m) promontory jutting westward into the sea just north of the Bay of Mont St Michel. It is 20 miles E of St Malo and only 9 miles from the Îles Chausey, to which day-ferries run all through the season.

Although there are still some fishermen operating from the harbour, recently it has developed more as a resort, especially for yachtsmen in the sheltered harbour on its southern side.

Approach   If coming from Jersey or the N, the right-hand edge of the town is the Pointe du Roc, with its 16m Grey lighthouse with R top at an elevation of 49m. The Lt is Fl (4) 15s. Stand about 3 cables off it on a SE'ly course to pick up Le Loup beacon (BW bands with disc topmarks) 24m high lying 3 cables S of the breakwater protecting the Avant-Port. The aerial picture (28.1) taken near HW (both locks are open) has Pointe du Roc just off frame, but shows Le Loup in the foreground. Its characteristics are Fl (2) 6s to a range of 11M.

Approaching from the W, head for the W-cardinal YBY whistle buoy marking an isolated rock at Le Videcoq. Its Lt is VQ (9) 10s. From this point head 090°. The port is 3½ miles ahead.

It is possible to enter the Avant-Port at half-tide in a boat drawing 1m50. The line of approach is to line up the Hérel marina breakwater Lt (Fl R 4s 7M—a W tower with R top) with a TV mast on 057° leaving Le Loup a cable to starboard. When the entrance to the Avant-Port is well open, alter to port and go for it between the breakwaters. The western arm has Iso R 4s 12m 7M on a W framework with R top. Its opposite number is Iso R 4s G and the W tower has a G top.

Berthing   You can lie alongside the western breakwater but it dries out. The locks with the Bassin à Flot open ± 1h on HW. This basin is primarily intended for commercial traffic, but, as the picture (28.1) shows, yachts can get permission from the HM (next to the lock on the E side) to go in, where there is a least depth of 4m, tel. (33) 50–12–45.

Access to the magnificent 850-berth Hérel Yacht Hbr, with 150 alongside berths reserved for visitors, is clearly shown by the electronic digital depth indicator situated near the end of the marina breakwater. When it reads 'O.O' the entrance is shut with a hinged gate keeping the water level inside at upwards of 1m7. When the tide has risen sufficiently to give 1m4 through the inner gate, the indicator clearly shows it and continues to act as a tide gauge. This arrangement is similar to that showing the water over the sill at St Servan.

The two poles marking the narrow entrance gate are 4m high and have Oc R 4s and Oc G 4s Lts respectively.

There is a large area (2½ × 1½ cables) south of the marina mole with sufficient water held in by a sill to enable the very active sailing school (CRNG) to function at all tides.

The marina office is in the splendid clubhouse of YC Granville. Contact on VHF Ch9 or tel. (33) 50–20–06.

Visiting yachts should make for one of the two pontoons directly in from the clubhouse: F or G.

Facilities   The clubhouse itself is sufficient for most crews' needs. There is a repair yard near by and a gridiron and travelhoist at the NE corner of the marina.

FW and electricity on all berths. Fuel at the head of pontoon G.

Taped weather forecasts on tel. (33) 50–10–00 and on display at the clubhouse. Area 11 Manche ouest.

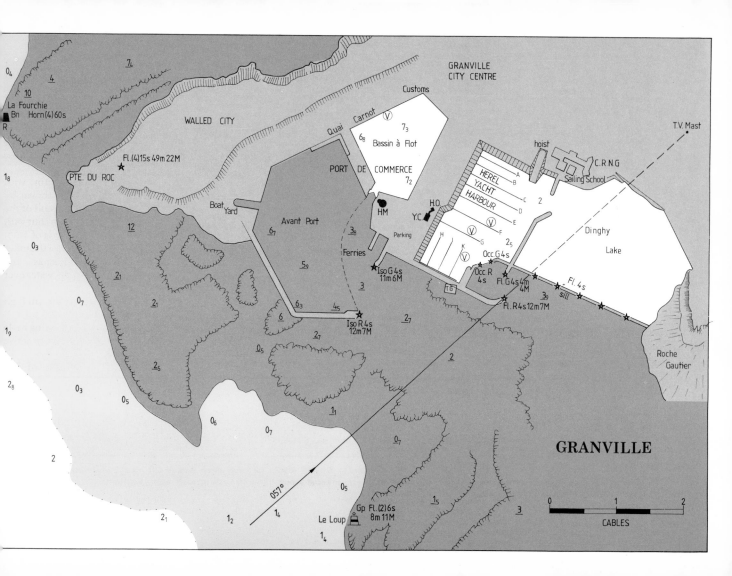

GRANVILLE

28.1   *The walled city of Granville near high water. In the foreground is the BW beacon Le Loup which must be left a cable to starboard on course for the new breakwater of Hérel yacht harbour. (A) is the Avant-Port. (B) is the Bassin à Flot which still attracts visitng yachtsmen. (C) is the boat repair yard. (D) Marina Office. (E) Visitors' berths.*

28.2   *The Avant-Port with walled city beyond. (Photo : French Government Tourist Office)*

Ferries for Jersey and Chausey berth just inside the Avant-Port, next to the marina car park.

Good hotels and restaurants. For an extra diversion there's always the casino—or the Aquarium.

29 CANCALE

Charts *CG 535 ; Fr 5644*
High Water *−05h 00 Dover* *−00h 15 SP St Helier*
Heights above Datum *Springs MHW 13m3 MLW 2m0*
Neaps MHW 10m3 MLW 5m1

THIS holiday resort and fishing port is better known for its oysters than its suitability for visiting yachtsmen. It is on the western entrance to the Bay of Mont St Michel, just 4 miles SSW of La Pierre de Herpin lighthouse off the Pointe de Grouin. The W tower has a B top and bars and it is 24m above sea level. Characteristics: Oc (2) 6s, 15M with a siren Mo N 60s.

La Houle, the little anchorage behind the 200m long Mole de la Fenêtre dries out to 7m5 but it might be possible to lie along-

29.1   La Houle anchorage for oystermen with its 200m long Mole de la Fenêtre and temporary alongside berths on the top half of the tide.

29.2 *Classy shops and bistros beyond the public landing point. (Photo : French Government Tourist Office)*

side for a couple of hours near the top of the tide (pic 29.1). There is a prominent disused light tower at the inshore end, while a W metal pylon with B top marks the southerly end (Oc (3) G 12s).

Head S from the Pierre de Herpin lighthouse for 3 miles when the Île de Remains will be abeam. If the wind is settled in a W'ly sector a good anchorage can be found ½ mile farther S of the rocky islands, but it is still 1 mile off the harbour entrance and the tide runs at 3 knots. At neaps one can safely anchor a lot closer.

Berthing and Facilities Ashore the CNC (Club Nautique de Cancale) may offer a mud berth, but it will be very exposed to the SSE.

There are some excellent fish restaurants near the landing.

Charts   *BA 2700 ; Fr 5645 ; Im C33b ; CG 535 ; Stan 16*
High Water   −05h 15 *Dover*   −00h 20 SP *St Helier*
Heights above Datum   *Springs   MHW 12m1 MLW 1m4*
                         Neaps   MHW 9m1 MLW 4m4

THE BAY of St Malo lies 30 miles S of Jersey separated by the notorious 'Minkies' (Plateau des Minquiers). It is the mouth of Le Rance, which leads into the canal system emerging at the mouth of the R. Vilaine into the Bay of Biscay about midway between the Morbihan and St Nazaire.

Behind a protective chain of rocky outcrops deployed up to 3 miles offshore, on either side of the river mouth are the towns of St Malo and Dinard. They could not possibly be more different.

Dinard is an Edwardian summer resort with shuttered, grand houses, sumptuous hotels set in tropical gardens and the sleepy elegance of another age. Right up to a generation ago it was the done thing to roll around at anchor in the Roads and row ashore to the slipway used by the vedettes plying to and from St Malo.

At that time the walled city of St Malo was being faithfully rebuilt in its original style (with indoor sanitation) after having been flattened in August 1944. Its inhabitants are fiercely proud of their history and traditions. They are 'Les Malouins' whose buccaneering explorers brought riches and glory home from the seven seas. In the New World they were the first to stake a claim on the islands now better known to Spanish-speakers as Las Malvinas—literally meaning the men of St Malo.

The restoration of the lock-gates in St Malo opened up a complex of deep-water basins, all named after those free-wheeling corsairs of the sixteenth and seventeenth centuries, and established St Malo as a major commercial and ferry port. Yachtsmen soon followed, and in due course the famous Cowes–Dinard Race had to change its name to incorporate St Malo. There was an embarrassing period in the 1970s when the prize-giving had to be duplicated by consecutive ceremonies on each side of the Rance.

Nowadays, with the addition of the huge marina in the sandy bay off St Servan, such moorings as Dinard has to offer to visiting yachtsmen are rarely taken up by British yachts.

Approach from the West   One look at a chart has made many a cruising yachtsman hesitate before visiting this most agreeable of all Britanny ports. In fact it is dead simple by day or night—except in thick fog—especially if one sticks to the main fairway from the NW.

A course of 135° from the SW Minquiers buoy for 15 miles or 7½ miles due E from Cap Fréhel fetches up at the St Malo Petite Channel whistle buoy (RWVS with disc topmark—Q). Two miles farther to seaward are the two buoys marking Le Vieux Banc: the W-Cardinal YBY one, Q (9) 10s and the N-cardinal BY bell buoy (QF). Here the tide starts running to the E +02h Dover (−5½h St Helier), turning W 6h later. Maximum rate 2 knots.

At the St Malo buoy, sail 130° 2 miles to the prominent lighthouse (le Grand Jardin) just to the west of the Île de Cezembre (33m high). The lighthouse is a Grey tower 38m high (Fl (2) R 10s 15M). The rear leading light, La Balue, is FG with a 25-mile range, but among all the city lights it is not easy to pick out, and it is 5 miles beyond le Grand Jardin. By day it is even more difficult.

It is easier to hold a steady bearing on le Grand Jardin, keeping clear to the eastward of les Courtis, a 21m G tower with a Lt Fl (3) G 12s. It lies ½ mile NW of le Grand Jardin. Leave it to starboard and, as you approach the main lighthouse, make a 2-point alteration to starboard to clear the lighthouse. It has a

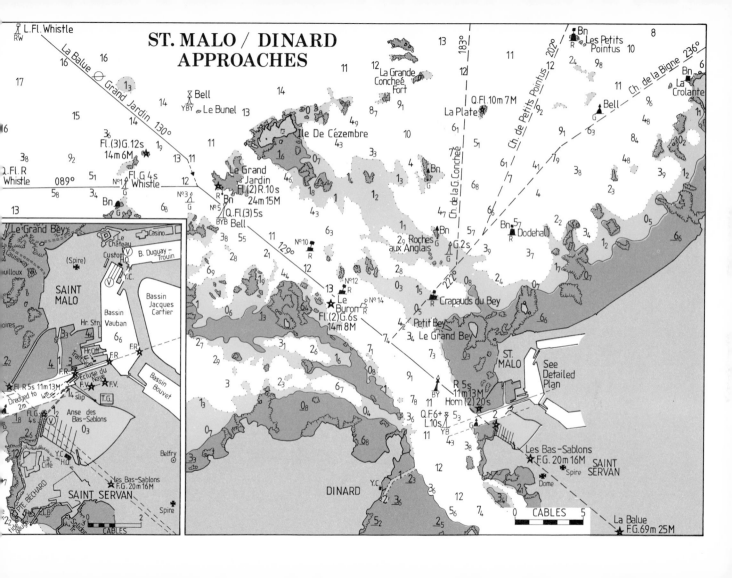

ST. MALO / DINARD
APPROACHES

30.1   Unusual aerial view from south-west. (A) Anse de Solidor on the Rance side of St Servan. (B) St Servan yacht harbour. (C) Les Bas Sablon front main channel leading light. (D) Lock-gates to St Malo. (E) Walled city of St Malo. (F) Bassin Vauban marina.

30.2 *Le Grand Jardin lighthouse with Red beacon immediately inshore.*

30.3 *Le Buron beacon-tower half-way to the harbour entrance.*

R beacon close to the S. As soon as the lighthouse bears NE, alter back to 130° so as to leave No.5 E-cardinal BYB bell buoy to starboard. Its Lt is VQ (3) 5s and has a bell.

It is on record that le Grand Jardin has a Radio Beacon on 294.2kHz callsign "GJ", but I have never heard it. Its claimed range is only 10 miles.

One mile beyond No.5 buoy is the stubby G tower 14m high called Le Buron (pic 30.3). Its Lt is Fl (2) G 6s 8M. It is opposite the R unlit No.12 buoy, with No.14 just beyond it, both to be left to port. If entering at night one can now pay some attention to the leading lights. Both are FG, the front one being a W square tower with B top above the St Servan Yacht Hbr; the rear one is La Balue, a 37m Grey square tower already described.

The only shoal water to be avoided is the Plateau de la Rance in the middle of the fairway. Its northern extremity is marked by a BY unlit N-cardinal buoy which must be left to starboard,

30.4 *Fort la Grande Conchée marking seward end of one of the approaches from the east. (Photo : Lt.-Com. O.M. de Las Casas)*

30.5 *Passing Môle des Noires with walled city in background heading for locks or St Servan.*

30.6 *Rounding the breakwater to enter St Servan yacht harbour with St Croix dome and front leading light almost in line.*

30.7   Boats berthed three abreast bows-south in the Bassin Vauban, as seen from the yacht club looking across to the walled city.

unless you are making to anchor off Dinard. It may be easier to head straight for the 10m high W tower with R top marking the SW end of the Moles des Noires, the main St Malo breakwater (Fl R 5s) making sure the tide is not setting you on to the unlit N-cardinal buoy.

Round the end of the breakwater on to a course of 075°, at which point the decision has to be made whether to go on into the Bassin Vauban alongside the walled city or to berth in the St Servan marina, locally known as the Port de Plaisance des Sablons.

Approach from the East   There are three suitable approaches from the E, either Granville or Chausey. While they save up to 3 miles against using the main channel described above, none is suitable except in good visibility by day and accepting that there is as little as 0m5 at LWS just before the junction of these NE approaches with the main fairway.

These channels are a lot simpler on departure, due to the distance to some of the unlit leading marks.

(a) *La Bigne Channel*   Start on the E-cardinal BYB buoy marking the Basse aux Chiens 1 mile NW of Pointe du Meinga

30.8 *Harbour Office in the Bassin Vauban. Apply here for times of going through the Rance barrage or getting a berth in the Bassin Duguay-Trouin.*

30.9 *Bridge open to go into the Bassin Duguay-Trouin where there is always room.*

and ½ mile ESE of the YBY Rochefort beacon tower. The course is 222° for 1¼ miles on a transit of La Crolante tower (a clear right-hand edge of land off Pointe de la Varde) with le Grand Bey (a rocky hump-shaped island just clear of the right-hand edge of the ramparts of St Malo). Half a mile short of La Crolante tower, alter to 236°.

This brings into line le Buron Tower (see above) and Villa Lonick 2 miles W of Dinard on Pointe Bellefard which has a W stripe painted on its face. As it is over 5 miles away it is better to concentrate on picking up a G bell buoy 7 cables beyond La Crolante. This is left to starboard.

Then, 3 cables on, alter to 222°, shaping to pass midway

between the R beacon in Grand Dodehal and the G buoy marking Les Roches aux Anglais. Next leave the R can-topped buoy marking Les Crapauds du Bey to port. This is the shallowest part of the approach. But 3 cables farther you hit the main channel about half-way between le Buron and the breakwater.

(b) *Petits Pointus Channel* Not so nail-biting in its early stages. About 1 mile W of the Rochefort beacon tower come on to 202° to leave the G bell buoy marking la St Servantine Rock to port. The transit is the right-hand edge of the fort on le Petit Bey in line with the Pointe de Dinard in the town itself.

Leave to port the R beacon marking les Petits Pointus rocks and straight on to join la Bigne channel at the R beacon marking

184

30.10 *Inside the Bassin Duguay-Trouin with the Harbour Office across the road on the left and the Quic-en-Groigne Castle in the background.*

Grand Dodehal rock.

(c) *Chenal de la Grande Conchée* One mile ENE of the Île de Cézembre is the prominent little flat-topped fort La Grande Conchée (pic 30.4). Leave it 3 cables to starboard on course 183° and La Plate Lt beacon close port. At the G conical buoy marking les Roches aux Anglais you join the other two channels on 222°. This channel is often used by the hydrofoils from Jersey. It saves 2 miles.

A large-scale chart shows several other rock-dodging channels,

but the ones described above will cater for the average yachtsman. For peace of mind I should always enter by the main NW channel past the Grand Jardin, but, if heading to the E take the Petits Pointus channel, providing there is sufficient water over the first $\frac{3}{4}$ mile.

Berthing

(a) *St Malo* Yachts berth either at the N end of the Bassin Vauban or the W end of Bassin Duguay-Trouin. For either it is necessary to enter through the lock between the RO/RO ferry

berth to starboard and the hydrofoil terminal to port. The HM is in a prominent control tower on the left of the locks. He is on VHF Ch12 and uses the following signals to govern traffic:

R flag or Lt: no entry
G flag or Lt: no exit
R and G flags or Lts: no movement
Flag P or W Lt to the left of the other: Gates open
Flag V indicates the movement of a ferry which, along with all other commercial traffic including fishermen, take absolute priority over yachts. They are not supposed to enter the lock without first being hailed.

Entry is normally $-2\frac{1}{2}$ HW and $+1\frac{1}{2}$h. Waiting buoys can be picked up on the N side of the approach channel to the lock-gates. There is a least depth of 6m3 inside.

There are no visitors' berths as such, so it's a matter of finding a space on any of the three long pontoons running S from the HO. No. 1 pontoon on its town side is for boats under 7m long. Boats over 11m long should either berth alongside the ramparts beyond the ferries or alongside the yacht clubhouse on the mole beside the entrance to the basin beyond (Duguay-Trouin). The bridge will be lifted to enter the latter.

Boats should berth three abreast, bows-S. Then report to the HO (pic 30.8)—tel. (99) 56–51–91—which is alongside the local Tourist Information Office.

The YC (SN Baie de St Malo) is hospitable and well accustomed to visitors from the UK. Its tel. (99) 40–84–42.

(b) *St Servan* If the new 720-berth marina at St Servan is preferred, just remember that there is a sill 2m above datum run

30.12   New jetty for landing from dredged mooring area off Dinard.

ning from the little breakwater on your starboard hand across to a point near to RO/RO berth. The depth of water over it is indicated by digital electronic display across the bay from the marina. Visitors should berth on the first pontoon inside the mole, clearly marked as such. The least depth is 1m7.

The HO is next to a little bar at the town end of the car- and boat-parking area near the travel-lift. The SNBSM has a club-house there (tel. (99) 81–78–01).

FW, fuel and electricity are available at both places. There are also chandlers and repair facilities near by.

The taxi fares to St Malo can mount up, but St Servan has plenty to offer hungry, thirsty or sleepy sailors unless their tastes run to the more sophisticated amenities of the city or they can't stay away from the casino. The hassle and uncertainty of the lock-gate operation is avoided.

Weather forecasts at the YC and HO, or by tel. (99) 46–18–77. Also on VHF Ch2. Area 11 Manche ouest.

(c) *Dinard*   There are no alongside berths at Dinard, but there is a 2m dredged area with moorings opposite the new quay (pic 30.12) clearly marked by perches with cardinal topmarks or buoys. The Dinard YC clubhouse is full of memories of the days when the big cutters used to race over from Cowes. (To this day the most sought-after trophy of the race is one given by Edward VII.) Tel. (99) 46–14–32.

The moorings are approached between three pairs of pillars leading in towards the White Ferries' landing ramp with a dredged depth of 1m.

FW and fuel can be obtained at the quay.

*31   DINAN VIA THE RANCE

Charts   *Fr 4233 ; CG Navigation Fluviale—Bretagne*

THE COMPLETION of the massive hydro-electric barrage across the Rance 1½ miles S of the entrance to St Malo opened up the first 3 miles as a peaceful cruising area with numerous attractive unspoilt villages to anchor off.

From the barrage to Port Dinan is 20 miles with one further lock to negotiate at Chatelier, only 3 miles short of your destination.

The old fourteenth-century walled town of Dinan sits 75m above the canal. Its 'harbour' is immediately downstream of the first bridge on the whole canal system, for which it is necessary

31.1   Entrance to the locks at the barrage across the Rance facing north with St Servan in the background. (Photo : Lt-Com. O.M. de Las Casas)

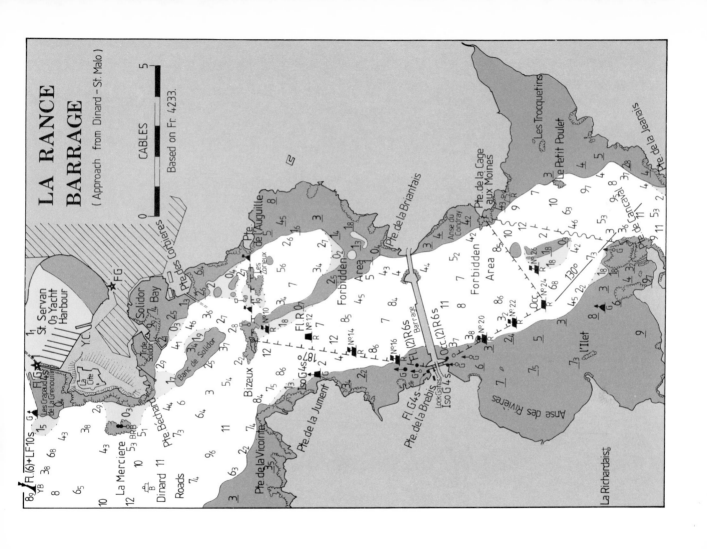

LA RANCE BARRAGE

(Approach from Dinard – St. Malo)

CABLES

0   5

Based on Fr. 4233.

31.2   The view upstream towards the artificial lake created by the barrage.

31.3   Slipway for landing at St Suliac on the east bank.

to lower your mast to negotiate the statutory headroom (2m50) for the remainder of the voyage southward.

It has a charm of its own and is well worth a visit even if you don't scale the heights to look down on the river from the Gothic castle.

Main Barrage and Locks Without local knowledge it is necessary to check in with the HM at St Malo lock-gates or the HO in the yacht marina in Bassin Vauban or at St Servan. There you will be given all the information on times of opening of the barrage and the second lock at Chatelier. It is imperative to pick up the printed instructions issued by the barrage authorities. A shortened version in English is also available, but the excellent Carte Guide—Navigation Fluviale gives it all in English as well. The electricity authority will give any further information required on (99) 46–21–87.

Briefly, the barrage locks can open whenever the level is 4m above datum, with a minimum of 2m0 in the lock. The back of the printed instructions give the precise times of the opening

31.4   The lock at Châtelier—three miles downstream from Dinan.

31.5   Berths on the west bank up-stream from Châtelier lock.

31.6   The old port of Dinan with many pontoon berths alongside. No need to climb the hill to the main town.

there and at Chatelier. Or the lock-keeper can be called on tel. (96) 46–21–87.

Normally the lock opens on the hour every hour when there is 4mo in the Rance basin at St Suliac (3 miles upstream). The lifting bridge which carries all the road traffic between St Malo and Dinard will be opened any time during the first 15min after each hour.

After 2000 and before dawn it is normally necessary to give 2h advance warning by telephone or to pull the bellrope at the lock entrance, which will respond with an illuminated panel 'Appel reçu'.

It is advisable to reach one of the waiting berths on the dolphins or lie in sight of the gates 20min before intended entry (pic 31.1). By night the NE dolphin has a Lt Fl (2) R 6s while the SE dolphin (upstream) is Oc (2) R 6s.

Approach   Leaving St Malo, make for the W side of the river and pick up the R beacon on Bizeux, a rocky islet ½ mile S of the landing point in Solidor bay on the S side of St Servan. Hereafter follow the channel leaving the R buoys close to port until reaching No. 16 just short of the lock-gates. La Jument, a G

31.7   The end of the road at Dinan, unless you have a tabernacle, draw less than 1m3 and want to go through the canals to Biscay.

tower on the W bank, is Iso G 4s, 6m high.

By day the locks will open when a B cone point downwards is displayed, or a G light by night. Coming downstream, a B ball or a R light are displayed. Outward-bound craft take priority.

Once inside keep within the marked channel. The farther you go the more it tends to favour the W bank.

It is outside the scope of this book to describe every village worth visiting along the way, but St Suliac on the E bank 3½ miles from the barrage is noteworthy (pic 31.3). Or an alongside berth 1m5 can be found at Mordreux.

To get through the second lock at Châtelier there needs to be 8m50 above datum. And before getting there a bridge with

least clearance of 19m needs to be respected by tall rigs. Ideally you should set off from the barrage 3h before HW. The lock-keeper at Chatelier can be contacted on tel. (96) 39–55–66 to double check.

Berthing and Facilities   Immediately through the lock the little village of Lyvet on the E bank has a slipway and an alongside berth, while there is a yacht anchorage against the W bank.

There are pontoon berths depth 1m6 on the W bank of the canal at Port Dinan, where FW and fuel can be obtained, to say nothing of an excellent meal in the Relais Corsaires, and adequate shopping.

The local port authority is on tel. (96) 39–04–87.

Charts *Fr 5646 ; BA 3659 ; CG 535, 536 ; (Im C33b)*
High Water *−05h 15 Dover* *−00h 20 SP St Helier*
Heights above Datum *Springs MHW 11m2 MLW 1m3*
Neaps MHW 8m5 MLW 4m1

ST CAST lies 4 miles SE of Cap Fréhel at the head of the drying-out bay of l'Arguenon and 7 miles WSW of le Grand Jardin, if sailing from St Malo. It is a fairly classy summer holiday resort, with a beautiful sweep of beach a mile long running from Pointe de St Cast to Pointe de la Garde.

Its attraction for passing yachtsmen is that there is good holding ground in 1m50 and even deeper close in towards the little harbour under the lee of St Cast point, while the quay is dredged to 1m50. Not recommended when the wind is between NE and S.

Even deeper water can be found off the landing at Pointe de la Garde where the YC de St Cast is situated.

The town has a monument overlooking it celebrating the day in 1758 when British invaders lost 2,400 killed.

Approach An E-cardinal BYB unlit buoy ¾ mile 070° from Pointe de St Cast marks Les Bourdinots rocks and lies in the G sector of the Iso WG 4s Lt on a 9m G and W structure at the end of the quay. Its range is 11M in its W sector and 8M in the G.

There is deep water to the S of that buoy; it is easier to leave it to starboard and stay in the W sector. The picture (32.2) shows the light structure at the end of the quay and the Bec Rond rocks close to the S; between them is the proper entrance.

If leaving Les Bourdinots to port, simply pass midway between the buoy and Pointe de St Cast.

32.1 Near-by Cap Fréhel is often the first landfall made by a yacht on passage from the West Country to St Malo.

32.2   A harbour for up to 1m5 draft, but not when the wind is between north-east and south. A view at low water.

By day a transit on course 216° of Bec Rond rocks and a church steeple on the skyline will bring you straight to the end of the quay. If going on to the anchorage S of Pointe de la Garde, hold off until the point with its conspicuous chapel bears due W and close on the echo sounder.

Berthing   Fishermen tend to hog the alongside berths at St Cast quay, but you could be lucky. Otherwise anchor, or pick up a buoy and argue about it later.

Facilities   There are new buildings at the inshore end of St Cast quay which house most things a visitor might need. The HO is there (tel. (96) 41–88–34).

FW available at the quayside.

There is a local boatyard and chandlery.

The YC at Pointe de la Garde (tel. (96) 41–05–77) also runs a sailing school.

Weather forecasts from the semaphore station above Pointe de St Cast (tel. (96) 41–88–34). Area 11 Manche ouest.

*33 ERQUY

Charts *Im C33b ; Fr 5724 ; (CG 536)*
High Water *−05h 20 Dover −00h 20 SP St Helier*
Heights above Datum *Springs MHW 11m2 MLW 1m3*
Neaps MHW 8m5 MLW 3m8

ERQUY is an active fishing port facing due W 8 miles beyond Cap Fréhel. It dries out completely and offers little protection from the prevailing seas except close inshore between the two breakwaters, where it is always packed out by fishing boats. It affords good shelter from the east.

Approach The approach is from due W bringing the ends of the two breakwaters in transit. By night it will lie in the W sector of the Oc (2 + 1) WRG 12s Lt on the 10m high W tower R top at the pierhead. The W sector has a range of 10 miles (pic 33.1).

Unless you're planning a brief visit on one tide or to dry out on an open beach with legs and walk ashore, Erquy is not recommended.

Facilities These are no great shakes, being geared to the needs of commercial fishermen. The HM is at the fish quay (tel. (96) 72–19–32). There are two slips. The local YC opens only in July and August.

Weather posted at the HO. Area 11 Manche ouest.

33.1 Not recommended except in settled weather and you are prepared to dry out well away from the fishing fleet.

PART FIVE

NORTH-WEST BRITTANY

St Brieuc — Brest

Soundings and heights in metres
Bearings and courses in degrees true
Distances at sea in nautical miles or cables

The coast is wild and rugged and utterly beautiful. . . . Most of the North Brittany coast is impenetrable to anything but the smallest craft, and then only in good weather, for the coast is defended by a great barrier of natural hazards.

. . . most of the perils lie near the surface, sharp reefs marked only by breaking water. These dangers reach out sometimes 12 miles from the land.

The coast is no friend to the sailor. Only those familiar with its dangers dare approach it with impunity.

Clare Francis, in her novel *Night Sky* (1983), writing about
wartime operations with few navigation aids functioning.

SAFE NAVIGABLE DISTANCES BETWEEN YACHT BERTHS, OUTSIDE ÎLE DE BRÉHAT AND ÎLE DE BATZ (in nautical miles)

	ST MALO	BINIC	PAIMPOL	TRÉGUIER	PERROS-GUIREC	MORLAIX	ROSCOFF	L'ABER-WRAC'H	LE CONQUET	BREST
ST MALO										
BINIC	33									
PAIMPOL	38	19								
TRÉGUIER	57	39	26							
PERROS-GUIREC	62	43	31	20						
MORLAIX	92	71	59	48	32					
ROSCOFF	85	64	52	41	26	13				
L'ABER-WRAC'H	117	96	84	73	58	46	33			
LE CONQUET	133	112	100	89	74	61	48	23		
BREST	150	129	117	106	91	78	65	40	17	

Charts *Fr 5725 ; Im C34 ; (CG 536)*
High Water *—05h 30 Dover* *—00h 30 SP St Helier*
Heights above Datum *Springs* *MHW 11m2 MLW 1m3*
  Neaps *MHW 8m5 MLW 4m1*

LE LÉGUÉ is the commercial port of the cathedral town and provincial capital St Brieuc. Its approaches dry out 2 miles to seaward and can be nasty during strong onshore winds. The port is mainly for fishermen and coasters serving the industrial complex on the outskirts of St Brieuc, but determined yachtsmen can find good shelter once locked inside.

Approaches At the southern end of the Baie de St Brieuc between Erquy and Binic is Le Légué RW whistle buoy with

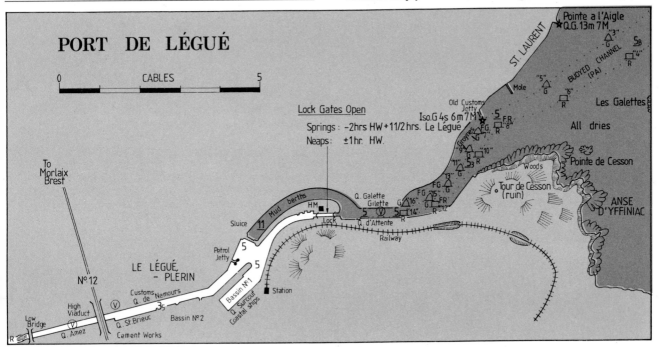

PORT DE LÉGUÉ

0   CABLES   5

Lock Gates Open
Springs : −2hrs HW+1½ hrs. Le Légué
Neaps : ±1hr. HW.

To Morlaix Brest

Pointe a l'Aigle
Q.G.13m 7M.

ST. LAURENT

Mole

Old Customs Jetty

Iso.G 4s 6m 7M

Les Galettes

All dries

Pointe de Cesson

Woods

Tour de Cesson (ruin)

ANSE D'YFFINIAC

Mud berths

Q. Galette Gilette

Q. d'Attente

Railway

Sluice

HM

Lock

Petrol Jetty

LE LÉGUÉ, - PLERIN

No 12

Customs Q. de Nemours

High Viaduct

Low Bridge

Q. Amez

Q. St Brieuc

Cement Works

Bassin No 2

Bassin No 1

Q. Surcouf Coastal ships

Station

34.1   Pte à l'Aigle lighthouse showing folly on left bank. (Photo : Lt.-Com. O.M. de Las Casas)

34.2   Lock-gates at Le Légué. (Photo : Lt.-Com. O.M. de Las Casas)

an Iso R 4s Lt. There is a lighthouse with W tower and G top on the N side of the entrance to Rue du Légué at Point à l'Aigle (Q G 13m 7M). Its arc of visibility is 160°–070°. The channel from the offshore buoy is marked by R and G unlit buoys. It has a depth of 3m at MHW neaps.

Entrance, Berthing and Facilities Yachts should pass through the commercial lock which opens $\pm 1\frac{1}{2}$h HW, rather less at neaps. Waiting for the locks to open you can secure alongside the Quai d'Attente port side to immediately outside the gates. The HM has his office alongside the N side of the lock. No.1 basin is only for commercial traffic, so yachts must go on to No.2 basin and berth where available immediately upstream, probably on the Quai Nemours, where there are Customs and all the replenishment and repair facilities a boat could wish for, although the surroundings are not particularly agreeable. There is a least depth of 3m in the basin.

The HM is on (96) 33–35–41. He also has VHF on Ch16 and 12.

Weather is on (96) 33–71–68. Area 11 Manche ouest.

34.3   Downstream view of berths at Le Légué under the N.12 viaduct.

*35 BINIC

Charts *Fr 5725; Im C33b; (CG 536)*
High Water *−05h 25 Dover −00h 30 SP St Helier*
Heights above Datum *Springs MHW 11m2 MLW 1m3*
Neaps MHW 7m4 MLW 4m1

BINIC, 7 miles NW of St Brieuc, is another popular summer resort with glorious beaches, where the yachtsmen have all but elbowed the fishermen out since lock-gates have been installed and pontoons providing 100 berths, with as many again in the Avant-Port or alongside the quays. Outside the harbour it dries at LW to a distance of ¾ mile. Normally the port can be approached any time during the top half of the tide, but operation of the lock is normally confined to the hour before HW. It is as well to check beforehand, especially around neaps (tel. (96) 73–01–86).

Approach First find the Roheim tower in the middle of the Bay of St Brieuc about 4 miles offshore. It is a 15m high Y tower with a B band and the topmark of a W-cardinal mark. Pass clear to the W and head WSW in the W sector of the VQ (9) WRG 12s light with a range of 10 miles.

By day leave well clear to starboard the E-cardinal buoy marking the Caffa bank. There's plenty of water to the S, so hold on until the W tower at the seaward end of Penthièvre mole (Oc (3) W 12s 12m 12M) can be seen and brought into line with the church steeple (see aerial pic 35.1). Then go for it. Two miles short of the harbour the W-cardinal buoy La Roselière will be left ½ mile to starboard as a check on the stream running at 2 knots parallel to the coast, turning NW at local HW.

Coming from the W there is a narrow passage close inshore through the Rade de Portrieux bringing one to a point 2 miles

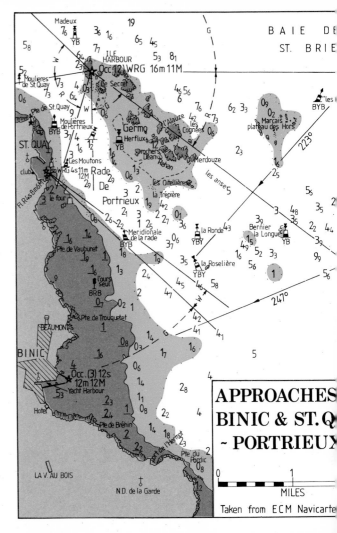

APPROACHES
BINIC & ST. Q
~ PORTRIEUX

0   1
MILES

Taken from ECM Navicarte

35.1   *The outer harbour should be accessible ± 3 hours high water.*

35.2 *As seen on passing outer breakwater head. The anvil-shaped structure to the left is the yacht club. Lock is open, bridge shut. Harbour Office is the small hut in line with the spire.*

35.3 *Close-up of the Harbour Office with the bridge open to allow yacht to enter.*

35.4   View of the yacht harbour from the yacht club. Note the town quay gives priority to fishing boats.

NNW of Binic, but it is easier on the ulcer to go E-about the off-lying rocks, leaving the E-cardinal Les Hors buoy to starboard. It lies 2 miles NNW of the Caffa buoy described above.

Once inside the breakwaters, hang about for the lock or take a temporary alongside berth, bearing in mind that it dries up to 6m.

On the left of the lock is the YC with a wide slipway on its seaward side. On the right is the small lock-keeper's hut just across the quayside from the little shack which is occasionally manned as the Bureau du Port. The Simplified Code is used to control traffic. There is no VHF. The gate is usually open when the tide is 9m.

Berthing   Visitors take their chance on finding a spare slot on a pontoon. Or berth alongside the quay and find the HM. There is ample water inside, reputedly 5m5.

Facilities   Besides the Club Nautique de Binic's small modern clubhouse, the town has everything on hand right along the quayside facing the pontoons.

FW and fuel available.

Customs are at St Quay-Portrieux.

There are two more slipways at the western end of the harbour.

Weather is posted at the YC and the Bureau du Port. Area 11 Manche ouest.

*36 ST QUAY-PORTRIEUX

Charts *Fr 5725; Im C33b; (CG 536)*
High Water *—05h 20 Dover —00h 30 SP St Helier*
Heights above Datum *Springs   MHW 12m2 MLW 1m3*
Neaps   MHW 8m5 MLW 4m1

THREE miles north of Binic is the popular seaside resort and home port of lobster fishermen of St Quay, with its drying-out harbour of Portrieux at its SE end. It has lovely beaches, smart restaurants and a casino for holidaymakers and a string of reefs and rocky islets 2½ miles long outside the front door for those hauling crustaceans.

Approaches Between the rocks (Roches de St Quay) and the harbour is a narrow but well-marked channel running parallel to the coast. At its SE end it forms the Rade de Portrieux. The current runs through this channel at over 2 knots at springs, starting to the NW at local HW (—05h 15 Dover) and turning SE'ly 6h later at local LW.

From the S follow the directions given for Binic until the unlit W-cardinal La Roselière buoy is abeam on course 320°. This will bring you towards the E-cardinal les Moutons buoy 2 miles to the NW, at which point it should be left to starboard, as course is altered to 260° for the harbour entrance.

From the N it is desirable to make for a point about a mile offshore on a SSE'ly course, leaving the W-cardinal beacon tower on the Madeux rocks to port. A mile farther S there is a promi-

36.1   Low water facing to seaward.

36.2   Why St Quay is planning a deep-water yacht harbour. (Photo : Lt.-Com. O.M. de Las Casas)

nent E-cardinal beacon to be left to starboard—les Moulières de Portrieux. From there it is ½ mile to les Moutons and the long N–S breakwater which gives the harbour its protection from most directions except the SE.

There are lights to point the way, but they should only be relied on in settled weather and after some local knowledge has been acquired. The NW end of the Roches de St Quay at Île Harbour has a 13m W square tower with R top and a Lt Oc (2) WRG 6s. The W sector from 080°–133° is visible at 12M and covers the safe water in the NW entrance to the channel. Its 8M G sector covers NW–E.

The seaward end of the main breakwater has an Iso WG 4s Lt from a prominent octagonal W tower with G top 12m above sea level. Its 12-mile W sector 3° either side of 309° marks the fairway from immediately inshore of La Roselière buoy to the harbour entrance, with a R sector to the E, and G to the W. The head of the other mole has a 6M Lt Fl R 4s from a 9m mast with a R top.

Berthing and Facilities   The whole harbour dries out at least 3m5 above MLWS. Fishing boats and local pleasure craft have priority for alongside berths, so you must be prepared to take the ground. There are several slips, those on the W side of the harbour for the considerable racing dinghy fleet attached to Portrieux YC. The HM is at the NW end of the harbour on Boulevard Marechal Foch, tel. (96) 70–42–27.

Fuel, water and provisions can all be obtained alongside. There are repair facilities and a 1.5-ton crane.

A new outer harbour with a least depth of 2m0 and free access at any state of the tide is planned to be built outside the NE breakwater with reclaimed land for a YC. When it happens it will transform St Quay-Portrieux as an attraction for visiting yachtsmen. (Present indications are that it will not be completed until 1987, if at all.)

Charts   *Fr 3670 ; BA 2557 ; Im C34 ; CG 537 ; Stan C16*
High Water   −05h 25 *Dover*   −00h 30 *SP St Helier*
Heights above Datum   *Springs*   MHW 10m3 MLW 0m5
                                     Neaps   MHW 7m8 MLW 3m2

PAIMPOL is another former home port for those who used to bring cod back from distant waters. Now only local fishing and oyster dredgers remain, while yachts increasingly take over the two basins behind the lock-gates.

The Bay dries out to a distance of 2 miles to the E, so it is essential to time one's arrival just before HW.

The town is 3 miles S of the Île de Bréhat, a 10min ferry crossing from Pointe de l'Arcouest, 6kms N of Paimpol.

Approach   To position oneself for the correct approach on the Chenal de la Jument on course 260° it is desirable to be on the right track 4 miles to seaward by picking up the BYB E-cardinal les Charpentiers beacon. It lies 1 mile NNE of the Lost-Pic lighthouse, a 20m W square tower with a R top (Oc WR 4s). Its W sector has a 10M range 16° either side of 237° from seaward. You are in the 7-mile R sector before bringing les Charpentiers beacon abeam to starboard.

If the wind is not NE–SE it is safe to drop the hook ½ mile inshore of the R buoy la Guele, bearing in mind that the tide runs SE–NW up to 2 knots. Unfortunately all the channel buoys are unlit. The charted transit by day is the Pointe Brividic (½ mile E of the breakwater) in line with the church tower on 260°. But a more easily identifiable transit is the W house on Pointe Porz-Don on the northern shore in line with a high column on the skyline on 269°. Porz-Don has a light Oc (2) WR 6s with a narrow 30 W sector 269°–272° and R to the left.

37.1   Paimpol at low water with inner lock-gate shut. (A) Bassin No.1 with small area (top right) for boats over 10 metres. The rest are in Bassin No.2 alongside the Harbour Office (B). The inner lock is dismantled and always open. Oyster dredgers on the mud in the foreground. Chandlery and boatyards at (C).

37.2   *The shabby Bureau du Port with the open lock to Bassin No.1 to the left.*

37.3 *Bigger boats in Bassin No.1.*

37.4 Bassin No.2 seen from the lock-gate. Slipway top right.

The final leading marks are the W hut with a R top at the seaward end of the main breakwater (Kernoa) in line with a 9m-high W lattice tower with R top on the shore beyond. Both have fixed R Lts. The rear one is intensified $2\frac{1}{2}°$ either side of the correct transit of 264°. This clears all dangers from la Guele inward. The channel is clearly marked by R and G perches with topmarks or small buoys all the way.

The final approach, once inside Kernoa Jetty, dries to 4m (aerial pic 37.1).

Normally the lock will open $\pm 1\frac{1}{2}$h HW, but at or near neaps it is nearer $\pm$30min or may not open at all. If in doubt, consult the harbour authority, tel. (96) 20–84–30.

Berthing The lock can handle craft with a minimum of 3m draught at neaps.

It is possible to dry out on the N side of the Kernoa breakwater while waiting, where it dries 5.5m. The two pontoons on the inner basin (No.1) reached through a dismantled lock are reserved for deep-draught yachts over 10m in length. The rest

of it is for commercial traffic. Coasters up to 1,000 tons call from time to time.

The remaining yachts berth in No.2 basin alongside the quays or at any of the 266 pontoon berths, of which a few are reserved for visitors.

The HO is on Quai Neuf dividing the two basins (pic 37.2) to which visiting yachts should report.

Facilities There are showers and heads near the local station of the Glénans Sailing School at the NE corner of No.2 basin. FW available at the quays.

The fuelling point is just to seaward of the lock-gate on the Kernoa breakwater.

There are several boatyards, a sailmaker and an excellent chandlery, all on the S side of the locks.

Good shopping and restaurants.

Weather is broadcast on VHF Ch84 at 0633 and 1133. Also posted at the HO, the YC and some chandlers. Area 11 Manche ouest.

Charts *BA 2557 ; Im C34 ; Fr 882 ; CG 537*
High Water *—05h 25 Dover*   *—00h 25 SP St Helier*
Heights above Datum *Springs MHW 10m4 MLW 1m1*
                          Neaps MHW 8m0 MLW 3m6

BRÉHAT is a group of small rocky islands with tropical vegetation, very popular with day-trippers, artists and owners of twin-keeled yachts. It is a navigator's nightmare, with sluicing tides running all round the islands. Perhaps it is better known as a hazard to avoid when making for the mouth of the Pontrieux river on the way to Lézardrieux.

However, given settled weather, it is well worth a short visit, especially if you like walking and want to get away from motor cars: none is allowed on the island.

Approach and Anchorages The approach from the Roches Douvres 17 miles to the NW is better explained in the chapter on Lézardrieux, which describes the longer-range navigational aids in the area. La Chambre and Port Clos are anchorages on the southern end of the main island. They are best approached from the E.

Coming from the N, shape 1 mile east of the Le Paon lighthouse (a 12m square Y framework tower at 22m elevation) and leave the E-cardinal Guarine buoy close to starboard on course 168°. This is the Chenal de Bréhat. A mile farther the BY N-cardinal Cain ar Mouse buoy will be ahead, at which point alter towards the left-hand edge of land and pick up the S-cardinal pillar off Logodoc island. Between it and the main island of Bréhat is a reasonably secure anchorage—La Chambre (pic 38.2). It is marked by R and G perches with topmarks.

Depending on space, you can anchor at the entrance in deep water and there is a landing.

Port Clos (aerial pic 38.1) dries out to its entrance. It is the terminal for the vedettes which run at a similar frequency to the Gosport ferry. One can be seen alongside the LW jetty on the western side. Just to seaward of it is the G-topped beacon marking Les Pierres Noires. Out of the picture 3 cables to the E is the YB W-cardinal beacon Men-Joliquet with an Iso WRG 4s Lt at 8m elevation.

Coming from the S it is best to leave les Charpentiers beacon (see Paimpol) and the W Cormorandière beacon clear to port on a N'ly course until sighting the Cain ar Mouse buoy (see above) and altering in towards La Chambre or Port Clos.

If making the trip from Lezardrieux, go downstream for 2½ miles until Levret Rock, immediately W of the little drying-out port at Loguivy is abeam. A course of 085° for just a mile should pass you close S of the BRB Rompa beacon. Le Ferlas channel is thereafter well marked by S-cardinal perches until reaching the relatively open water S of Port Clos. The tide runs to the E +01h 05 after HW Dover; turns W at —05h 10 before HW Dover at a spring rate of 3¾ knots.

Port de la Corderie lies to the NW of the island. It is approached along the main channel to the Pontrieux River (225° or 045°) until the prominent R la Corderie beacon is found off the westernmost point of Bréhat at the white Roseda pyramid day-mark. Head in towards this pyramid until the Men-Robin perch is identified and left well clear to starboard on a SSE'ly course. Observe the R and G beacons until in the jaws of the bay, where deep water can be found N of the Kalex G beacon. But it is necessary to tuck into the bay to get away from the strong tides running down le Kerpont channel to the west. A good afloat anchorage at neaps.

Berthing and Facilities There are no alongside berths for yachts on the islands.

38.1 Port Clos on the south end of the island, with the vedette using its low water landing opposite Les Pierres Noires beacon. The hotel and the high water landing is at the head of the bay. La Madeleine and Men ar Gouille port-hand beacons are on the right of picture.

38.2 La Chambre anchorage is reasonably deep at its entrance. See right of picture.

The YC at Guerzido, east of Port Clos, is the Club Nautique de Bréhat.

An ideal spot to go ashore for a walk or even a picnic, but not for too long unless you keep your boat in sight. There are two small hotels, one of them in Port Clos by the HW vedette landing.

The usual amenities one would expect on a remote little beauty spot which dies in the winter—somewhere between Chausey and Arran in this respect.

Charts *BA 2557 ; Fr 2845 ; Im C34 ; CG 537 ; Stan 16*
High Water *−05h 10 Dover −00h 30 SP St Helier*
Heights above Datum *Springs MHW 10m0 MLW 0m9*
Neaps MHW 7m5 MLW 3m4

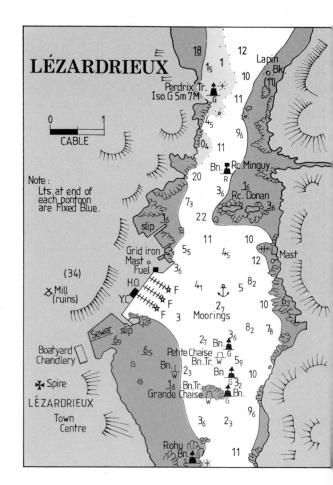

LÉZARDRIEUX

Note :
Lts. at end of
each pontoon
are Fixed Blue.

LÉZARDRIEUX'S great attraction for visiting yachts from the South Coast is that it provides an alongside berth in perfect shelter accessible from the open sea at all states of the tide and in bad visibility, provided you hit off one of the outlying buoys. If it is your first visit, a night approach in clear visibility is easiest. Thereafter it is straightforward, since the channel beacons are at short intervals. I once came from St Malo in visibility under a cable, happened upon the N Horaine spar buoy and had no problems. The market town is perched on a high bluff overlooking the Pontrieux River (more frequently referred to simply as 'Trieux') on its western bank. It has a first-class hotel and gourmet restaurant, but these are a long uphill walk from the 220-berth marina just downstream. The town itself is of no special interest.

Approach Coming from the South Coast or the Channel Islands you will find there are several off-lying roadsigns for checking that one is on course. The first and most prominent of these are the Roches Douvres (pic 39.1) whose 70-mile range Radio Beacon on 298.8kHz callsign "RD" booms out in the same group as Start Point and the Casquets. Its Lt (Fl 5s) has a range of 28M, more than enough to cover the 15 miles to the entrance of the Trieux River on a SW'ly course after leaving the Lt to starboard. The structure is a 60m pink tower on a G-roofed house. It also has a siren ev 60s.

In good visibility and after taking a careful look at the state

39.1   Unmistakably Roches Douvres 15 nautical miles north-west of entrance to Trieux River on course from the Channel Islands. Seen from the west.

of the tide and currents, it is all right to head 210° to pass 1½ miles west of Barnonic an octagonal BY light tower 19m high with an E-cardinal topmark and a Lt VQ (3) 5s, range 8 miles. It lies 5 miles due S of Roches Douvres. If in doubt, for example in heavy weather or fog, stand a mile farther to the west until clear to leave the next mark to port.

A mile farther on is the W-cardinal YBY Roches Gautier whistle buoy (VQ (9) 10s) which lies 6 miles NNE of the first of the local buoys marking the Plateau de la Horaine 3 miles NE of the low-lying Île de Bréhat.

By night one is already well within the coverage of another four lighthouses:

La Horaine A 20m B octagonal tower, Fl (3) 12s with a range of 11 miles. It lies 1 mile south of the N-cardinal BY spar buoy marking the northern limit of that danger.

Rosedo light on the NE corner of Bréhat, a 13m W tower at 29m elevation. The Lt is Fl 5s with a range of 20 miles. It also has a rather feeble Radio Beacon (callsign "DO" on 294.3kHz, the same as le Grand Jardin off St Malo). I have never been able to pick it up. Its notional range is 10 miles.

Les Heaux de Bréhat off the mouth of the Tréguier River and 4 miles W of the approach course to Trieux. It consists of the very conspicuous 57m-high Grey tower with a Lt Oc (3) WRG 12s. Closing the coast one will first be in the W sector at 15 miles. As you come into the G sector (10 miles) the end of the runway is right there. It is best to arrive on the E-setting flood stream (+01h 35 on HW Dover).

Le Paon at the NE corner of Île de Bréhat, demolished by some over-zealous German defender in 1944 but since rebuilt as a Y square tower. Lt FWRG with a range of 12 miles in the narrow W sector only 7° either side of 188°.

There is also a 50-mile Aerobeacon inland to the W of Tréguier on 345.5kHz, callsign "LN".

Now one should be on 225° with the R can-topped beacon

39.2   *Down-river view with Trieux yacht marina and the deep water channel between Roc Donan (right) and Perdrix Tower on the west bank. Note number of yachts anchored off the fairway downstream.*

9.3   *Trieux Yacht Club with Bureau du Port incorporated.*

Les Echaudes $\frac{1}{2}$ mile to port. The Grand Chenal leading marks are La Croix beacon due W of the southernmost point of Bréhat (a W structure with R top and Lt Oc 4s) lined up with a W house with a G roof 2 miles upstream on the W bank. Its Lt is Q W, range 21 miles.

The Lts are intensified either side of 225° as follows:

Front (la Croix):   10°
Rear (Bodic):   4°

From here on it is quite straightforward, between R and G prominent beacons. Half a mile upstream of la Croix beacon there is a YBY W-cardinal beacon marking the western approach to Bréhat (Le Ferlas Channel). Here course is adjusted to 219° on to another transit of two W-gabled houses on the W bank. The front one is Coatmer at 16m elevation; the rear one only 3 cables farther on is 50m above sea level. Both have narrow FR sectors when you are on course.

9.4   *Pontoon berths off yacht club looking upstream.*

Abreast of these marks a further alteration to port is needed to negotiate les Perdrix, a prominent G beacon on an elbow on the W bank. It has an Iso G 4s Lt.

At les Perdrix point, come to starboard so as to leave the prominent Donan rocks to port (aerial pic 39.2).

Berthing One can anchor almost anywhere off the fairway in the lower stretch of the river, but the marina has 220 berths with least depths of 1.8m up to 2.5m.

It is administered from the HO in the hospitable little YC (YC du Trieux), tel. (96) 20–14–22. There are also some visitors' buoys reserved in the middle of the river.

Facilities The YC and a local waterfront bistro will look after most of your needs without walking up to the town. FW and fuel are available at the pontoons. The commercial quay next to the marina has a 6-ton crane, a gridiron and a slipway.

Almost next door is Trieux Marine, a boatyard and chandlery which can handle most repairs.

Weather forecasts obtainable by phone: (96) 20–01–92. Area 11 Manche ouest.

*PONTRIEUX is 6 miles farther inland from the bridge across the river at Lézardrieux (clearance indicated by tide gauge, but never less than 18m) there is the small market town of Pontrieux with an unexpected industrial complex supplied by quite sizeable ships.

If you want a peaceful diversion there are deep alongside berths (minimum 3m2) on the quay along the E bank (pic 39.6).

The lock-gates are 1 mile downstream from the town. The channel up from Lézardrieux winds its way through lonely countryside reminiscent of the upper reaches of the Dart. It is intermittently marked by perches. Since it nearly dries out, obviously one should time one's trip in the last 2 hours of the flood.

It would be advisable to enquire first at the YC du Trieux

39.5 *Pontrieux locks facing upstream with inner gate open. Note factor* *beyond.*

or the HO. They will give you the times of opening of the loc (usually ± 1hr HW) and probably give warning of any shippin movements due.

Berthing and Facilities Berth alongside the quay as fa upstream as possible.

FW and fuel are available.

There is a local YC on the quayside, but not as smart as thos one is accustomed to in the new French Yacht Hbrs.

There is a restaurant near the YC, but a brief walk into th old town centre will give a wider choice and all kinds of shop banks and a main post office.

39.6 *Plenty of water alongside at the 'Port'.*

39.7 *Just around the corner from 39.6, where the navigable water ends at the bridge from which this picture was taken.*

40 TRÉGUIER

Charts *Fr 972, 973 ; Im C34 ; (CG 537)*
High Water *—05h 40 Dover* *—00h 55 SP St Helier*
Heights above Datum *Springs* MHW 9m7 MLW 0m9
Neaps MHW 7m4 MLW 3m3

TRÉGUIER, like Lézardrieux, is accessible from the open sea at any state of the tide at the end of a well-marked 7-mile passage from the off-lying dangers. But this town is much larger and more interesting. It features a huge cathedral dating back to the thirteenth century, named after St Tugdual. Here lies the tomb of St Yves, the patron saint of lawyers and protector of the poor and persecuted since he was born in Tréguier in 1253. 'Monsieur St Yves' is how he is referred to even nowadays.

Approach On passage from the South Coast or Channel Islands the instructions given for Lézardrieux apply, except that the course to make good after leaving the Roches Douvres to starboard is 230°—18 miles to the landfall buoy (La Jument, a N-cardinal BY bell buoy VQ flash). One should be in the W sector of les Heaux de Bréhat light (Oc (3) 12s 48m 12M) for most of the way, although if you are too close to the Roches Gautier the R sector may show briefly.

Some 2½ miles SW of la Jument buoy is the prominent Crublent R buoy, a whistler Fl (2) R 6s with a 5-mile range. Leave it on the starboard bow and shape up for Grande Passe leading marks and Lts on course 137°. They are difficult to distinguish by day, on the E side of the estuary 3–4 miles distant, as follows:

Front: Port de la Châine, a W house at 12m elevation Oc 4s 12 miles

Rear: Ste Antoine, another W house with R roof at 34m elevation. Its Lt is Oc R 4s 15M which is intensified ±3 either side of 137°.

Passing between R and G unlit channel buoys on the transit, it is exactly 1 mile to the G Penar Guezec buoy, also unlit, when course is altered to 215° towards La Corne light beacon 14m high, a pepper-grinder W tower with a R base. Its Lt is Oc (2) WRG 6s, range 9 and 6 miles—the narrow (7°) W sector brings you safely along the first 1½ miles of the river entrance. R means you are too far to the E; G to the W of track (i.e. to starboard going in).

A W beacon tower (St Keiviec) 4 cables farther upstream should be kept just open to the right of La Corne.

On the unlit G channel buoy just past La Corne, take a ½-mile hitch on 235°. At night this will be in another narrow W sector of La Corne Lt, with R on either side of it, which can be confusing.

From the next port-hand buoy (No.2 Fl R) alter to 192° with 3½ miles to go to the Yacht Hbr alongside the town. From there on, the channel is well marked with R and G buoys and beacons. The port-hand R buoys all the way to No.12 have dim R Fl Lts, while the starboard-hand G Fl are numbered 1—11.

At night the final approach calls for a 2-cable SW'ly leg from the last lit buoy, then a hitch to the SE towards the E bank of the river opposite the marina. A light with a strong beam is essential.

The least depth is 2m6 in the channel.

Inshore NE channel—Passe de la Gaine If coming from Bréhat or Lézardrieux in good visibility by day about 1½ miles can be saved by using the Passe de la Gaine, the inshore passage inside Les Heaux de Bréhat on course 242°. A glance at the chart will show that it is very tight and passes over a 0m3 patch at MLWS. However it is a possible alternative when outward bound, given close attention to the chart and benign weather.

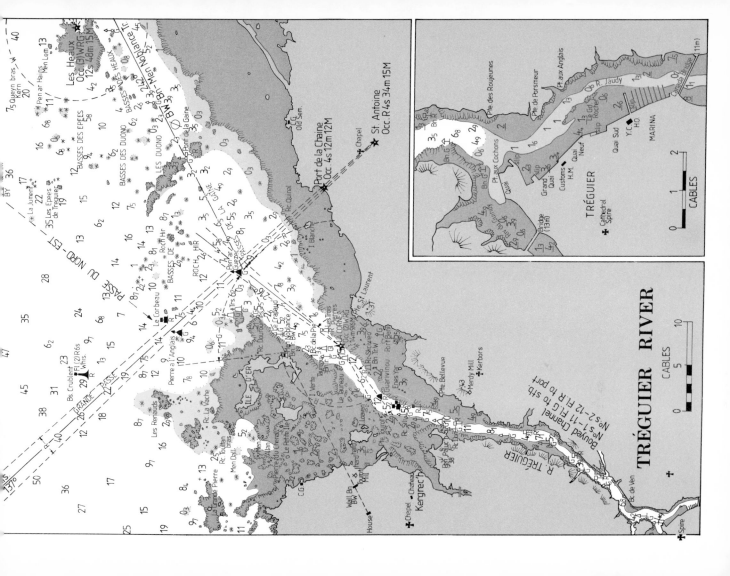

40.1 *(A) Yacht Club du Trégor with harbour office. (B) commercial quay. (C) last port-hand buoy. (D) starboard-hand buoy. Follow white course line.*

40.2   Yacht club pontoons facing upstream.

The astern leading marks are the Grande Maison and BW wall beacon on the skyline in transit the conspicuous BW tower beacon to the W of the channel (Men Noblance) on 062°.

Berthing   The long quays at the foot of the town are clearly set aside for commercial traffic. Just upstream are the five pontoons of the Club Nautique de Trégor (CNT). There are 300 alongside berths in an average depth of 2m at LW. Visitors should make for the first two pontoons beyond the slipway (pic 40.2). Remember that the streams run through these berths at up to 2½ knots, so great care is necessary in manoeuvring in or out not to get tangled up with other boats. There is a luxurious clubhouse on the shore end of these pontoons also housing the HO (tel. (96) 92–42–37). There are also moorings on the E side of the river near the bridge, beyond the old low-level viaduct,

now mostly demolished.

Facilities   The clubhouse has everything the visitor could wish for.

FW and fuel available.

There is a boatbuilder and good heavy chandler at Plouguiel just across the river, but Marina Sports next to the YC is a well-stocked chandlery with a repair staff.

Weather reports at the clubhouse or tel. (96) 20–01–91. Area 11 Manche ouest.

Beside its cathedral and cloisters, the town has two good hotels and a selection of small restaurants. There is also the usual open market once a week, selling everything from day-old chicks to ten-year-old Calvados.

223

Charts *Fr 974 ; Im C34 ; CG 537*
High Water *−05h 50 Dover* *−01h 05 SP St Helier*
Heights above Datum *Springs* *MHW 9m0* *MLW 0m9*
Neaps *MHW 7m0* *MLW 3m4*

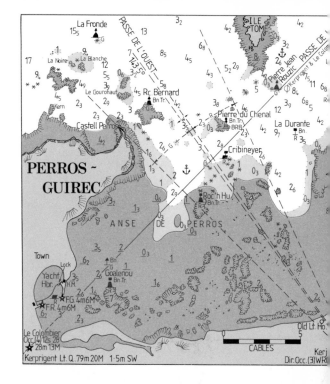

PERROS-GUIREC is a major summer resort with wonderful beaches about 10 miles W of the entrance to Tréguier River. Since the artificial Yacht Hbr has been built, the town's discos, pubs and sportsgear shops have proliferated in the marina area, while the luxury hotels and fashionable restaurants are mostly near the Casino, beside the N-facing beaches some distance away.

The whole bay dries to a mile offshore at LW.

Approaches Before making the run in towards Perros-Guirec from seaward it is as well to check the times of opening of the lock-gates unless you are prepared to take the bottom exposed to the E, or lie alongside the Linkin Jetty which protects the marina from the NE–SE. Here it dries at least 4m.

As a rule the lock will be open at springs from 2h before to 1h after HW, while at ordinary neaps it will only open during the hour before HW. At bad neap tides it may not open at all. So check first with the HM near the lock-gates, tel. (96) 23-19-03.

From the NE (Passe de l'Est) Two miles NW of Port Blanc is the R buoy Roche Gauzer. Left to port on course 224° it is a 5-mile run-in from there, the first 3 miles being in deep water until passing S of the Île Tomé and leaving the G Pierre Jean Rouzic buoy close to starboard.

At this point the leading marks ashore should be clearly visible, certainly by night since they have ranges of 16 and 13 miles respectively, as follow:

Front: Le Colombier a W gabled house 28m above sea level with a Lt Oc (4) 12s intensified 5° either side of the leading line, precisely 224½°.

Rear: 1½ miles farther inland on the transit is the W Kerprigent tower 79m above sea level with a Q Lt with a 7° intensified arc either side of the leading course.

41.1   *Seaward end of Linkin breakwater with Red Goalenou tower beyond. The sill enclosing the yacht harbour on left.*

41.2   *Lock-gates with big schooner taking fuel just inside.*

41.3　Some of the 650 berths on pontoons with least depth 4 metres.

Half a mile farther the BRB isolated danger beacon Pierre du Chenal is left to starboard, before the last 1½ miles to the head of the Linkin breakwater (Fl (2) G 6s) and the lock-gates after a sharp turn to starboard round its end (pics 41.1 and 41.2).

From the NW (Passe de l'Ouest) A mile NE of Ploumanach put the light on the westernmost of les Sept Îles astern on a course of 143° to the Île Tomé and the point of Perros-Guirec. Leave the R tower Petit Bilzic to port and two further G channel markers to starboard before joining the Passe de l'Est SW of Pierre du Chenal (see above).

At night there is a directional Lt of 78m elevation at Kerjean (Oc (3) WRG) with less than 1° W sector at 12-miles range.

By day the disused lighthouse on the foreshore at Nantouar can be brought in line with Kerjean lighthouse on the skyline.

Berthing Once locked into the Bassin à Flot you will find there are 650 berths on the pontoons, 40 of them reserved for visitors. The least depth is 2m. One can also anchor to the E of the pontoons. The HO by the locks will direct visitors; tel (96) 23–19–03.

Facilities There is a fuelling berth just inside the lock-gates The Yacht Hbr is in the middle of town with everything on tap. There is a slipway at its northern end.

The YC—Societé Nautique de Perros-Guirec at Ploumanach (SNP)—has a clubhouse by the Yacht Hbr and another (for dinghies and sailboards) at Trestraou beach on the northern side of town.

Chandlery and light repairs are readily available.

The weather is posted at the Bureau du Port or a taped message can be obtained on tel. (96) 20–01–92. Area 11 Manche ouest.

*42 LANNION

Charts *Im C34 ; CG 537 ; (Fr 5950 ; BA 2644)*
High Water *−06h 05 Dover SP Brest*
Heights above Datum **(river entrance)**

Springs	*MHW 9m1*		*MLW 1m3*	
Neaps	*MHW 7m2*		*MLW 3m5*	

HEADING westward between les Sept Îles and Ploumanach (near Perros-Guirec) on the 20-mile passage to Roscoff and the entrance to the Morlaix River, keep well to seaward of yet another rocky, inhospitable headland. Provided the wind is not in the W–NW sector you might be tempted to take a look at Lannion, a medieval town of some interest 4 miles up the R. Léguer, sometimes referred to as the Lannion River.

Just N of the river entrance is the holiday resort of Trébeurden which has two YC, mainly for shoal-draught cruisers, dinghies

42.1   Alongside berths are not very attractive at low water at Lannion.

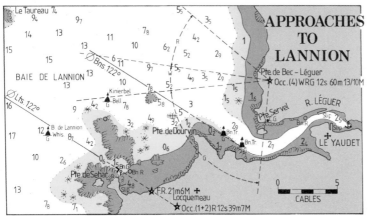

and sailboards. It has over 300 moorings, some reserved for visitors, but shelter from the weather is entirely provided by the rocky outcrop which encircles the W-facing beach and hardly invites penetration by a keelboat.

Approach   About 3 miles SW of Trébeurden is Le Crapaud, a W-cardinal YBY buoy. Half a mile south of this buoy come on to the 122° transit of the lights at Locquémeau. The front structure is a 19m-high W lattice tower with R top. Its Lt is FR. The rear Lt (Oc (3) R 12s) is a W gabled building on high ground (39m). Before reaching the G Locquémeau channel buoy, head due E towards the prominent low W house at Bog-Léguer 60m above sea level, which has an Oc (4) WRG 12s Lt— the W sector being 7° either side of the correct lead inshore. Two prominent G beacons will be seen on the starboard bow. Alter to 122° to pass close N of both of them. There is 3m of water off them.

Follow the bend in the river round to port for a distance of ¾ mile from the second G beacon. Leave a R beacon to port and you will be off the attractive little village of le Yaudet on the S bank.

Berths   It is possible to anchor and stay afloat in 2m off le Yaudet. The next 3 miles up-river should only be attempted in the last 2h of the flood. Just short of the first bridge (Pont Neuf) it is possible to lie alongside quays on either bank, but the river dries up to 5m at this point and it is not a very attractive spot to stay for any length of time (pic 42.1).

Facilities   There are landing slips on both banks at le Yaudet, where there is an agreeable little hotel/restaurant. The town centre of Lannion is a tidy walk beyond the mud berths described above, but there are good shops and hotels there.

The harbour authority is at tel. (96) 37–06–52.

The local airfield is only 1½ miles out of town.

*43 MORLAIX

Charts *BA 2745; CG 538; Im C35; Fr 5827*
High Water −06h 10 Dover +01h 05 SP Brest
Heights above Datum (river entrance)

	Springs	MHW 9m0	MLW 1m3
	Neaps	MHW 7m0	MLW 3m5

MORLAIX is a sixteenth-century town at the head of the river of the same name 7 miles inland from its entrance. An old viaduct above the town dominates the scene, matched by a new one carrying the N12 autoroute to the W. Between the two there is a perfectly sheltered Yacht Hbr (aerial pic 43.5).

In more recent times it has become an important centre of the tobacco industry.

Approach The most frightening part of the approach is at the river mouth between Carantec on the W side and Térénez opposite it. Right in the middle is the fort (Château du Taureau) built in 1542 to discourage the British from making further raids up the river (pic 43.1). Once it has been safely left astern there is a well-marked deep-water channel between the oyster beds to the point where the river narrows between Locquénolé and Dourduff, 3 miles downstream from Morlaix.

From seaward there are two main channels. The Tréguier channel from a point 1½ miles due W of Pointe de Primel near the G perch marking the Pierre Noire rocks. It is absolutely straightforward by day any time except within an hour of LW, since there is a ½-mile stretch which all but dries out at springs. It reaches the deep water midway between the Île Noire and the Château Taureau.

Alternatively, there is the Grand Chenal favoured by commercial traffic, since there is not less than 3m at any state of the tide. This channel starts 3 miles west of Primel, half-way to Roscoff, between the G la Vielle beacon and the R pillar buoy, both unlit, marking the Stolvezen shoal.

Each shares as the inshore end of their leading marks the

43.1   Île Louet and Chateau du Taureau seen from the south-west. The Grand Chenal passes between these two.

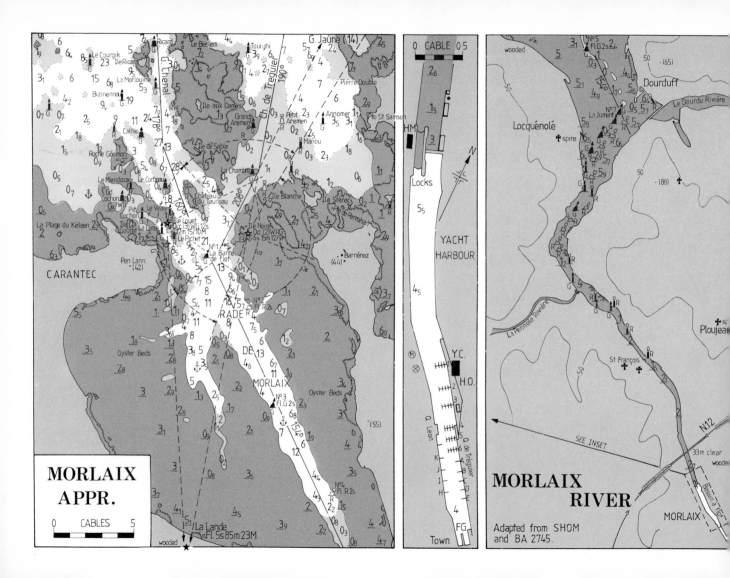

MORLAIX
APPR.

0   CABLES   5

MORLAIX
RIVER

Adapted from SHOM
and BA 2745.

43.2 *The alternate channel (Tréguier) leaves Île Noire tower clear to port before joining the main channel. I. Stérec and the last Red channel buoy to the left and beyond.*

43.3 *Rade de Morlaix facing upstream with Dourduff and viaduct to the east and Locquénolé opposite, where the river begins.*

43.4 *Dourduff with La Jument No.7 buoy off the point.*

prominent square W tower la Lande lighthouse, 19m high at an elevation of 85m a little over 2 miles due S of Château Taureau. This is the strongest Lt in the area with a range of 23 miles. It flashes 5s.

Grand Chenal lines up la Lande on 176° with the Île Louet 13-mile Lt (Oc (3) WG 12s) a square W tower with B top on an islet off Carantec (pic 43.1); a two-point jink to port has to be made between two prominent R and G beacons immediately to seaward of Chateau Taureau, on course 160° heading for the G unlit No.1 channel buoy. Although this is a deep-water channel, it is very narrow, less than a cable wide. From No.1 buoy (la Barre de flot) the course is 150° down the fairway.

Chenal de Tréguier lines up la Lande on 190° with Île Noire light, a 13m high W square with a R top with a Lt Oc (2) WRG 6s. The channel comes in on the R sector with a range of 9 miles. The shallow water referred to above is between the first pair of prominent but unlit G and R beacons. At la Chambre, leave the

43.5 *This downstream shot shows Loquénolé top centre on the west bank, the N12 viaduct, lock-gates and Morlaix Yacht Club with its pontoons.*

43.6   Upstream from the locks.

43.7   Berths on the east bank.

second G beacon to starboard, alter to 210° to pick up the main channel at No.1 channel buoy 3 cables beyond the Île Noire light-house (pic 43.2). A back bearing of la Chambre (G) and Petit Aremen (R) beacons in transit will bring you into the deep channel.

Thereafter the course is 150° with Fl channel buoys until No.5 buoy just short of Dourduff. From this point the channel is clearly marked by channel buoys or perches.

A lot of summer moorings are occupied off Locquénolé and Dourduff. From this point one's progress should be adjusted to reach the Morlaix locks while they are open, 1½h before until 1h after HW, when there will be not less than 2m5 at the entrance.

Berthing   There are pontoon berths for 160 boats, with room for plenty more alongside the quayside. The HO is on the E bank and keeps watch on VHF Ch9.

Alternatively the HM at the lock-side can be contacted on tel. (98) 88–01–01.

Visiting yachts should berth anywhere and report to the HO in the YC.

It is a secure, quiet harbour in any weather.

43.8   Sheltered berths right in the heart of town.

Facilities   The YC de Morlaix (YCM) has everything laid on, tel. (98) 88–17–61.

There are a yacht yard and several chandlery stores. Weather forecasts available on (98) 88–34–04. Area 11 Manche ouest. The town centre is ¼ mile farther upstream, beyond the first of two town bridges which have no more than head room for inflatables or dinghies.

There are several luxurious old hotels, plenty of restaurants, including some specialising in oriental food.

There is a local airfield at Ploujean and only 28km by fast road to Roscoff and the Brittany Ferries' connection to Plymouth. Although not the quietest or most picturesque of marinas, I rate Morlaix as an ideal place to leave one's boat if sharing its use with another crew or wanting to park it with complete confidence for a few weeks between spells of cruising. It is only 60 miles to the northern end of the Chenal du Four.

Charts *BA 2745; CG 538; Im C35; Fr 5828*
High Water *−06h 05 Dover* *+01h 00 SP Brest*
Heights above Datum *Springs* MHW 8m9 MLW 1m3
Neaps MHW 7m0 mLW 3m5

ROSCOFF nowadays is best known for the RO/RO Plymouth ferry terminal at Port de Bloscon, 7 cables east of the old harbour. It is firmly out-of-bounds to yachts, in spite of its tempting deep water close inshore.

It is the departure point for Johnny Breton on his bike, festooned with strings of onions, once a regular feature of our South Coast lanes. Recently its reciprocal trade from British farmers has been less welcome.

It is also whence the local ferry sails on its 15min trip to the Ile de Batz close to the N. The whole area is embraced by the Gulf Stream with concomitant sub-tropical vegetation. It is surrounded by unfriendly rocks, which are equally famous for their lobsters and shipwrecks. The sixteenth-century church is worth a visit. Apart from any other attraction, it is close to an outstanding restaurant which deserves, but does not get, a nod from the Guide Michelin.

The harbour dries out completely and the approach is hair-raising, but Roscoff is a neat, friendly little town which should not lightly be left out of one's cruise plan if the tides work out and it is not blowing from the NE.

Approach
From the NE One's ETA should be planned during the last 2h before HW, since the inner harbour dries 5m0 and many of the off-lying rocks are a menace at half-tide (aerial pic 44.1). There is a Radio Beacon at the RO/RO ferry terminal—callsign

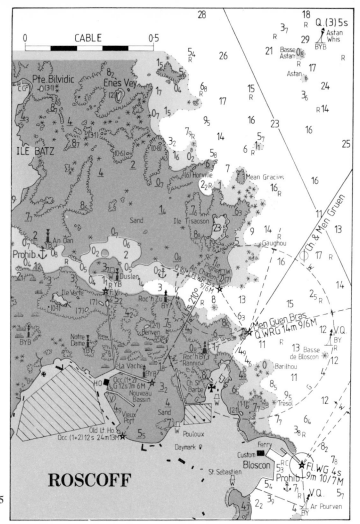

Ø 210°

44.1   From the north-east almost on the leading line for harbour entry (see dotted line from old lighthouse at the head of the harbour). Note rocks well outside the two beacons on the left (Men Guen Bras and Roch Rannic). Ar-Chaden light tower bottom right.

44.2 *Old lighthouse.*

"BC" on 287.3kHz with a range of 10 miles, but that is only marginally helpful.

Keeping clear to the N of the Plateau des Duons on a transit of 256° Men Guen Bras light tower in line with the bell tower of the church near the right-hand edge of Roscoff, it is necessary to find the other light tower which pairs off with Men Gruen Bras to mark the front door at 5 cables from the harbour entrance:

Men Gruen Bras is a YB tower with N-cardinal topmark, 20m high and a 9-mile Lt Q WRG. Keep in the W sector.

Ar-Chaden just 2 cables NW of Men Gruen Bras is equally prominent and the same height. It is YB with S-cardinal topmark and a 9-mile Lt Q (6) + LFl WR 15s.

If on the transit with Roscoff church it is necessary to alter to starboard to go close to Ar-Chaden light as the aerial picture (44.1) shows. Then pick up the transit of the light on the seaward end of the main (W) breakwater with the prominent square tower

44.3 *Nouveau bassin. Berths reserved for commercial craft.*

44.4   Yachts dry out in the Bassin du Vieux Port.

lighthouse on the waterfront on course 210°. Their characteristics are:

Breakwater light: Oc (3) G 12s 7m 6M.
Shore lighthouse: Oc (3) W 12s 24m 15M.

From the West On passage from the sea buoy off L'Aber-Wrac'h it is 31 miles to Roscoff by passing north of the Île de Batz, as against 28 miles if one takes the inshore passage between the island and Roscoff. The latter is a 3-mile passage with not much sea-room in the event of a sudden drop in visibility in tides running up to 3½ knots. I should never attempt it unless everything was set fair.

However, if bound to the west, the Île de Batz channel is fairly straightforward in settled conditions. Ideally it is best attempted in the last hour of the flood, so that navigation can be conducted in relatively slow time. The tide turns to the W at 1h after HW Brest (−06h on Dover) so an hour before HW Brest would be a good time to go. The channel is well marked but has the advantage of presenting its trickiest problems in the first mile after leaving Roscoff harbour on the back-transit of 210°/030° used for entry. Just short of Ar-Chaden alter to 280°, then shape to pass close N of the BY N-cardinal Roch Zu beacon before clearing the end of the 600ft-long pier used by the Île de Batz ferry when the tide water in the harbour is insufficient.

Here course should be altered to starboard to 290° to leave to port the BY Per Roch BY beacon with N-cardinal topmark. A mile farther, on 265°, pass between the YB S-cardinal Roche la Croix and N-cardinal BY l'Oignon beacons. A further mile of 285° should leave the N-cardinal BY Basse Plats to port, whence you are in deep water and can go for L'Aber-Wrac'h, the Chenal du Four or the Scillies, as may be desired.

Berthing It is tempting to berth alongside the outer mole in the Nouveau Bassin, but don't count on staying there. Fishermen and the vedette to the Île de Batz take—indeed enforce—their priority. So it is best to take the ground after finding a spot alongside the inner mole in the Vieux Port.

Facilities There are a boatyard and all kinds of mostly touristy shops. Plenty of good little hotels and restaurants.

The HO is near the Vieux Port on tel. (98) 61–19–59. Customs are at the RO/RO ferry terminal at Bloscon.

The local YC is Société de Régates de Roscoff on (98) 69–75–16. Weather is posted there and at the HO. Area 11 Manche ouest.

For a change of scene an outing up the R. Penze to visit Carentac and the Île Callot is recommended—in a dinghy and outboard.

Charts *BA 1432 ; Fr 5287 ; Im C36 ; CG 540*
High Water *+05h 40 Dover* *+00h 25 SP Brest*
Heights above Datum *Springs* *MHW 8m0* *MLW 1m1*
Neaps *MHW 6m1* *MLW 2m9*

OF THE three river-mouths at the NW corner of Finisterre—
Aber-Wrac'h, Aber-Benoit and Aber-Ildut—the first named is
best known to visiting yachts from the UK. It is easy to find and
straightforward to enter in anything but NW'ly gales. The
amenities ashore are limited, but the estuary forms a lovely
tranquil setting only 15 miles from the Chenal du Four—like
Balham, the Gateway to the South.

Approach Just 3 miles ENE of the sea buoy of L'Aber-
Wrac'h is the Île Vierge, a massive landmark with its 83m lighthouse and 70-mile Radio Beacon on 298.8kHz, callsign "VG".
It is in the same group as Roches Douvres and the Lizard but,
maddeningly not as Ushant (308.0kHz callsign "CA"). The Lt
is Fl 5s and can be picked up at 28 miles, or two-thirds of the
way from the Lizard. It also has a foghorn ev 60s.

Although charts show leading lines along the Chenal de la
Pendante and the Chenal de la Malouine, it is simplest to hold
on the W beyond Île Vierge until the W-cardinal YBY Le Libenter buoy is picked up. It has a Lt Q (9) 15s. Leave it to port
on a southerly heading until picking up the Grand Chenal on
course 100°. This will bring into transit the W square tower R
top on the Île Vrac'h (elevation 19m and 7-miles range) with
The very conspicuous Lanvaon lighthouse 2 miles father inshore.

Its 27m square tower is 55m above sea level and painted W
on its western side. Its Q Lt has a range of 10 miles. The Lt
is intensified 10° either side of the transit.

*45.1 A view inward-bound on the Chenal de la Pendante. Grand Pot de Beurre
almost in transit with the Petit Pot. (A) is Île Vrac'h. (B) is Breac h'Ver. Chenal
de la Malouine leaves two small marks to port. (C) is L'Aber-Wrac'h.*

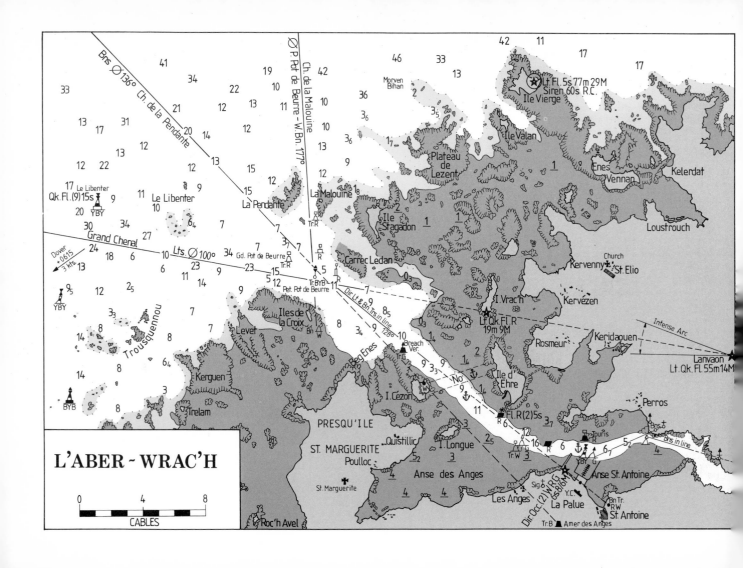

L'ABER - WRAC'H

CABLES

0 4 8

15.2   *L'Aber-Wrac'h lifeboat slip and pontoon opposite yacht club. Last channel buoys at bottom right.*

45.3 *Low water at slipway next to yacht club.*

About $1\frac{1}{2}$ miles from the Libenter buoy there are the R beacon tower Grand Pot de Buerre and the E-cardinal Petit Pot de Beurre BYB beacon both to be left close to port.

At this point, alter to starboard to 128° to follow the main channel leading straight for the point of land on the western bank where the village of L'Aber-Wrac'h is situated. The lifeboat shed and slip are prominent, almost right ahead. Alongside is a Lt Oc (2) WRG 6s on a W concrete tower. The W sector is only $\frac{3}{4}$ of a degree either side of the glide path, with a $1\frac{1}{2}$° G sector indicating off course to starboard and $1\frac{1}{2}$° R when off to port. By day the light tower lines up with two RW unlit beacons beyond it. From this point it is $2\frac{1}{2}$ miles to go, but there is a least depth of 3m5 at LW if you leave the G beacons to starboard and R to port.

Approaching from the E in good visibility, 2 miles can be saved by taking the Chenal de la Malouine. Keep $\frac{1}{2}$ mile offshore from the Île Vierge until you have identified the R Grand Pot de Buerre Tr. Then bring the Petit Pot de Beurre E-cardinal Tr in transit with a conspicuous W obelisk on the Île de la Croix on course 176°. Hold that course to leave the Petit Pot close to port when you are in the Chenal de la Pendante described above.

Berthing and Facilities Just beyond the prominent lifeboat house and its launching slip is the sumptuous new YC presiding over a single pontoon with berths for 80 yachts (1983). There are moorings for many more offshore and a dinghy slip.

The clubhouse is also the home of the HO: tel. (98) 03–91–62. Weather is posted there. Area 11 Manche ouest.

There are limited shops, but one memorable local restaurant. Bonded stores can be obtained here.

FW and fuel are available.

*46 LE CONQUET

Charts BA 3345 ; Fr 5287 ; Im C36 ; CG 540
High Water +05h 35 Dover As for SP Brest
Heights above Datum Springs MHW 7m2 MLW 1m4
Neaps MHW 5m6 MLW 2m9

LE CONQUET is a pretty little fishing port at the southern end of the Chenal du Four between the group of islands which include Ushant and the western tip of Brittany. The channel is famous not only for its sluicing tides running up to 5 knots at springs, but also because it provided the German battle-cruisers *Scharnhorst* and *Gneisenau* with their escape route from Brest, when the RAF's surveillance suffered from defective radar and the 'tin ring' of our submarines failed to make contact, in spite of ignoring the Admiralty Sailing Directions' caution that the area off Pointe St Mathieu 'is prohibited to submerged submarines'.

We always assumed that we lost two of our submarines there, until one of them was found in 1983 just off the Isle of Wight.

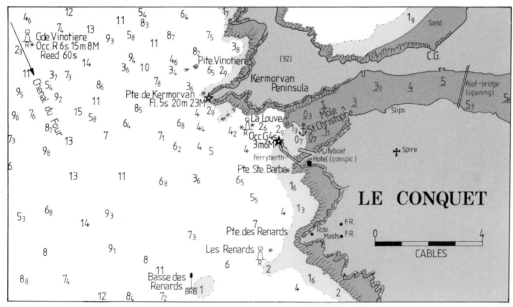

243

46.1 *Approach from north-west leaving Kermovan lighthouse and La Louve beacon to port. Note ferry is alongside outer breakwater and room left for it to turn.*

46.2 Ferry jetty unoccupied. Lifeboat Station and hotel dominate middle of picture.

46.3 Kermovan Light looking to seaward with Grande Vinotière beacon on the Chenal du Four beyond.

Le Conquet is a useful port of refuge if you just miss the tide all the way through and don't want to divert 17 miles to the new Yacht Hbr E of Brest.

Approach From the sea buoy off L'Aber-Wrac'h it is just 20 miles to Le Conquet. The Chenal du Four is a deep-ship channel and marked accordingly. Give Le Four Lt a fair bit of sea room, especially if the tide is still flooding (up to 1h before HW Dover) when it will be setting you onshore. The Lt is a Grey tower 28m high, Fl (5) 15s to a range of 20 miles. It has a siren (5 ev 75s). Thereafter head SSW for the Chenal de la Helle, which is the northern part of the Chenal du Four. Leave to port the lighthouse marking Les Plâtresses 2½ miles NW of Pointe de Corsen. The lighthouse is a 23m W tower Fl RG 4s range 6 miles.

Then pick up the main transit on 138° aligning Pointe de Kermorvan at Le Conquet (a W square tower—pic 46.3—20m above the sea, Fl 5s to a range of 23 miles) with the prominent Lochrist octagonal W tower with R top (Oc (3) 12s) set 49m above sea level.

This will bring you straight to the end of the new outer breakwater with an Oc G 4s Lt at its northern end. There is an unlit R beacon to be left to port at the entrance.

Berthing There are no readily-available alongside berths, although the new ferry dock just inside the breakwater may be

46.4   Moorings in outer harbour.

46.5   Slipway in old (inner) harbour, which dries.

tempting. The vedettes run back and forth to Ushant, and they swoop round the corner, confident that they won't find a visiting British yacht secured there.

There is over 2m water off the ferry berth, and the shoal water, which dries out, is a cable farther inshore. You could pick up a buoy there or anchor close NE of the breakwater if the weather is settled. Allow room for the ferry to back off and slew round to starboard.

Otherwise you must be prepared to take the ground beyond the inner mole (St Christophe), which is the fish dock, and land there or at the slipway beyond.

Facilities   The local harbour authority is at Rue A-Lucas, tel. (98) 89–00–05.

A local garage can provide an electrician or a mechanic. FW and fuel available.

The weather is posted on the quayside. Brest–Le Conquet weather broadcasts are on 1673kHz at 0733, 1633 and 2153. The general weather on Radio France (1071kHz) is put out at 0725 and 1850. Area 12 Ouest Bretagne.

There is a spectacular hotel hanging on the edge of the cliff facing due W. It is a favourite with businessmen from Brest (24km by road) for lunch, or coachloads of Gallic grockles, and wedding parties at the weekends.

The town itself is unspoilt and has the usual crêperies and Breton pubs decorated with fishnets and old lobster pots.

Charts   *Fr 6542 ; BA 3427 ; Im C36 ; CG 542*
High Water   *+o5h 1o Dover   SP Brest*
Heights above Datum   *Springs   MHW 7m5   MLW 3m0*
                          Neaps   MHW 5m9   MLW 1m4

BREST is a major naval base and commercial centre of 250,000 inhabitants. It lies on the N shore of the spectacular natural setting of Brest Roads, which provide over 40 square miles of sheltered water, ideal for day cruising.

There are numerous little coves where one can anchor along the 10-mile approach from Pointe St Mathieu (4km S of le Conquet). But the massive artificial harbour in the heart of the city does not welcome or accommodate yachts, which must carry on a further 2 miles to the E to the new Yacht Hbr at Moulin Blanc.

In any case it is to be preferred to berthing in the main port, which is a bit like taking a yacht into Liverpool or Marseilles.

Brest figures in the history books, mostly due to disagreements with the British going back to the fourteenth century when it was swapped for one of Charles VI's daughters.

Its most troubled times were more recently. As a German naval base on the edge of the North Atlantic, it was pounded to pieces by Anglo-American air raids. When it was finally liberated, three months after D-day, we acquired a heap of rubble. Hence the wide range of new buildings which form the city centre today. It is also the headquarters of the French Hydrographic Service (SHOM).

Approach   Pointe St Mathieu is the equivalent of Cape St Vincent (pic 47.1). At St Mathieu you turn 90° to port to run along the coast to Brest. It is deep water all the way and very well marked. The lighthouse at Pointe St Mathieu is unforget-

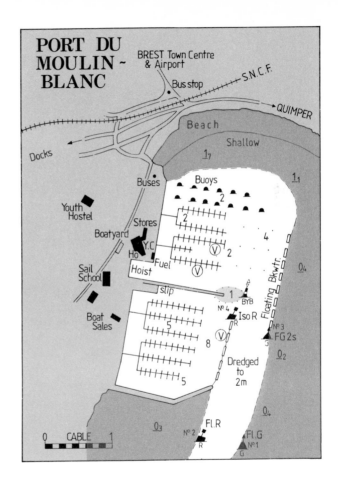

47.1 *Pointe St Mathieu marking the point to head east for Brest. Lighthouse is built out of an old ruin.*

table: a 37m W tower with a R top built out of the ruins of an old abbey. It is 56m above sea level (Fl 15s range 29 miles). It has a Radio Beacon on 289.6kHz, callsign "SM" with a range of 20 miles.

There is a secondary light with a lesser range Q WRG 14.10.9 miles. When you are in the 22° G sector it is time to start altering to the E and leave Les Vieux Moines Lt (Oc R 4s) to port—another octagonal tower.

17.2   *Looking eastwards over Pointe du Portzic with naval port nearest and commercial harbour beyond. (A) is the A-Louppe bridge. Port du Moulin Blanc is round the corner at (B).*

47.3   *Rounding floating breakwater to enter the yacht harbour.*

47.4   *Some of the 730 pontoon berths.*

47.5   *The yacht club, surrounded by stores, agencies and boatyards.*

The rest of the approach is straightforward. Leave the naval and commercial harbours to port and head 065° towards the Pont Albert Louppe carrying the N165 highway southward towards Quimper. Nos 2 and 4 R fairway buoys should be left to port. Their lights are Fl (2) R 6s and Oc R 4s. The next buoy is S-cardinal (Q (6) + LFl 15s). A mile beyond it is the R Moulin Blanc buoy (Oc (2) R 6s). Here alter slowly to port until you can lay 005° to pass between MB1 and MB2 buoys which mark the final short 3-cables channel to the new Yacht Hbr at Port du Moulin Blanc. They have Fl G and Fl R lights, while MB3 is Fl G 2s and MB4 is at the end of the floating breakwater, showing Fl R 2s.

Berthing and Facilities   Entering on a N'ly course between two lines of floating pontoon breakwaters there is an E-cardinal buoy to be left to port before going straight to the visitors' berths on the first two pontoons in the N Basin, right in front of the stylish clubhouse, which also accommodates the HO.

Call on VHF Ch9 or 16, tel. (98) 02–20–02.

There is a minimum of 2m water in the North Basin. Altogether there are 800 berths, 730 of them alongside pontoons.

FW and fuel readily available. A 14-ton travel-lift. The YC—Société des Régates de Brest (SRB)—is right there, with an excellent restaurant and every facility a visiting yacht can wish for. If you don't like your boat, there is a large stock of new ones to choose from.

Weather forecasts on (98) 84–63–00. Also, see Le Conquet. Area 12 Ouest Bretagne.

Brest is on the main SNCF railway line and has an airport at Guipavas only 10 minutes from the marina.

APPENDIX
Where to buy charts and publications

French Navy Charts (Fr)   published by le Service Hydrographique et Océanographique de la Marine (SHOM).
By post from:
A l'établissement Principal du SHOM, Section deliverance, B.P.426., 29275 Brest Cedex.   (tel. (98) 03–09–17)
Main agent in Northern France : Heilmann, Port des Yachts, Bd. Clémenceau, 76600 Le Havre (next to the Yacht Club at Le Havre.
They also hold a stock of British Admiralty charts).
Main agent in UK : J. D. Potter, 145 Minories, LONDON EC3N 1NH.
Nearly every chandlery carries a selection of SHOM charts. The following are in the area covered by this book:

Dunkerque	Weizsaeker et Carrère	30, rue du Leughenaer (59140 Dunkerque). (28) 66–64–0
	Dekyspotter M.R	14, rue des Fusiliers-Marins, B.P. 1049 (59375 Dunkerque). (28) 65–98–33
St Valéry-sur-Somme	Hall Nautique de la Baie de Somme	(80230 St-Valèry-sur-Somme). (22) 27–53–64
Rouen	Papeterie du Port	68, quai du Havre (76000 Rouen). (35) 71–45–82
Le Havre	Heilmann (voir agent distributeur) Nautic-Service	23–27, rue A. Barbes (76600 Le Havre). (35) 26–40–40
Ouistreham	Accastillage Diffusion	Port de plaisance (14150 Ouistreham). (31) 96–07–75
Caen	Caen Marine	9, boulevard Bertrand (14000 Caen). (31) 85–70–36
Cherbourg	Nicollet	40, rue du Commerce (50100 Cherbourg). (33) 53–11–74
Granville	Roquet	22 rue Le Campion (50400 Granville). (33) 50–09–34
	La Marine	2, rue Saint-Sauveur (50400 Granville). (33) 50–71–31
Saint-Malo	Back	5, rue Broussais (35402 Saint-Malo). (99) 40–91–73
	Voilerie Richard	3, rue du Glorioux (35400 Saint-Malo). (99) 81–63–81
	Sablons Yachting	Port des Bas Sablons (35400 Saint-Malo). (99) 56–98–17
	Librairie Nautique des Bas Sablons	26, rue des Bas Sablons (35400 Saint-Malo). (99) 81–06–60
	L'Ancre de Marine	4, rue Porcon (35400 Saint-Malo). (99) 56–78–43
Saint-Brieuc	Accastillage diffusion	4, rue Baratoux (22000 Saint-Brieuc). (96) 33–96–36
Plérin	L'Habitat et la Mer	28, rue de la Tour (22190 Plérin). (96) 33–71–68
Binic	Jean Bart Marine	quai Jean Bart, BP 15 (22520 Binic). (96) 73–75–28
Paimpol	Le Corre L	rue de Romsey (22500 Paimpol). (96) 20–85–17

Perros-Guirec	Ponant Loisirs	La Rade (22700 Perros-Guirec). (96) 23–18–38
Lannion	Lesbleiz S.A	Route de Guingamp (22300 Lannion). (96) 37–09–12
Morlaix	Jegou Ritz	10, place des Otages, B.P. 186 (29204 Morlaix). (98) 88–04–15
Brest	Jouanneau	75, rue de Siam (29200 Brest). (98) 80–17–07
	Berra Michel	6, rue Porstrein (29200 Brest). (98) 80–49–74
	Belmar	quai Commandant Malbert (29200 Brest). (98) 44–39–61
	Fonderies Phocéennes	4, rue Amiral Troude (29200 Brest). (98) 44–84–69

Carte Guide (CG)   Navicarte Éditions Cartographique Maritimes are available at any Librarie Maritime and at all chandleries, including those listed above. For corrections or further details, write to:

Navicarte E.C.M., 9 quai d'Artois, 94170 Le Perreux-sur-Marne

Admiralty charts (BA) are sold through agents listed on pages 230–3 of *The Shell Pilot to the South Coast Harbours*. They are also published quarterly in the Small Craft edition of Admiralty Notice to Mariners.

Imray Yachting Charts (Im)   are available at most outlets carrying BA charts. Some of their stockists are listed below:

Great Britain

Bath	Anchor Marine	1 Sussex Place, Widcombe, BA2 4LA
Bournemouth	A.H.F. Marine Ltd	934 Wimborne Road
Burnham-on-Crouch	Kelvin Aqua	The Quay, Essex
Brighton	Marina Watersports	Brighton Marina, BN2 54F
Bristol	Tratman & Lowther	Berkeley Palace, Clifton
Chichester	Yacht & Sports Gear Ltd	13 The Hornet, PO19 4JL
Christchurch	Rossiter Yacht Builders Ltd	Bridge Street, BH23 1DZ
Clacton-on-Sea	Anglo Marine Services	Forse Lane Ind. Est., Essex
Cowes	Groves & Guttridge Chandlery Ltd	127 High Street, PO31 7AY
	Pascall Atkey & Son Ltd	29–30 High Street
Dartmouth	The Bosun's Locker	24 Lower Street
	Cobbold Marine	The Quay
	Dartmouth Chandlers	24 Foss Street, TQ6 9DR
	Harbour Bookshop	Fairfax Place, TQ6 9AE
Dover	Dover Marine Supplies	158–160 Snargate Street, CT17 9BZ
East Looe	Jack Bray & Son	The Quay

Emsworth	The Bookshop	The Square, PO10 7EJ
	Wheelhouse Chandlery	51 High Street, PO10 1LA
Exeter	Devon Boats Ltd	Haven Road, EX2 8DP
	Eland Bros	22 Bedford Street
Falmouth	Bosun's Locker	Upton Slip, Church Street
	Falmouth Yacht Marina	North Parade, TR11 2TD
	Marine Instruments	50 Arwenack Street, TR11 3HL
	M & P Miller	15 Arwenack Street, TT11 3JH
Folkestone	Forepeak	Fishmarket, Kent
Fowey	Guerniers	3 Station Road, Cornwall
Guernsey	David Bowker	Pier Steps, St Peter Port
	Channel Island Yacht Services	North Esplanade
	Marquand Bros Ltd	North Quay, St Peter Port
	Navigation & Marine Supplies	North Plantation, St Peter Port
Gosport	Hardway Marine	95–99 Priory Road, Hardway, PO12 4LF
Hayling Island	Dinghy Den Ltd	66b Elm Grove, PO11 9EQ
	Sparkes Boatyard Co Ltd	38 Wittering Road, Sandy Point, PO11 9SR
Havant	West Havant Marine	43 West Street, PO9 1LA
Ipswich	Ancient House Bookshop	25–27 Upper Brook Street
	Ipswich Marina Ltd	The Strand, Wherstead, IP2 8NJ
Itchenor	H.C. Darley & Son	PO20 7AU
Jersey	Gorey Yacht Service	Gorey Pier
	South Pier Shipyard	St Helier
Kingston-on-Thames	The Boat Shop Ltd	Kingston Bridge, Hampton Wick, KT1 4BZ
Lancing	Compass Marine Services	145 South Street, BN15 8BD
Littlehampton	Britannia Watersports	Fisherman's Quay
London	Arthur Beal	194 Shaftesbury Avenue, WC2N 8JP
	Force 4 Chandlery	30 Bressenden Place, Buckingham Palace Road, SW1 5D
	Greenwich Marine Ltd	22 College Approach, SE10
	Ivory Marine	Eastgate House, St Katharine's Dock, E1
	Kelvin Hughes Ltd	31 Mansell Street, E1 8AA
	London Yacht Centre	13 Artillery Lane, E1 7LP
	J. D. Potter Ltd	145 Minories, EC3N 1NH
	Edward Stanford Ltd	27a Floral Street, WC2W 9LP

	Telesonic Marine Ltd	60/62 Brunswick Centre, Marchmont Street, WC1
	Captain O. M. Watts Ltd	48a Albemarle Street, Piccadilly, W1X 4BJ
Lymington	Berthon Boat Co	The Shipyard, Bath Road, Hants
	The Boathouse	The Quay
	The Haven Boatyard	Kings Saltern Road, SO4 9QD
Milford-on-Sea	Tony Redfern Marine	27 High Street, SO4 9QF
Paignton	Torbay Sail & Power Boat	The Harbour, TQ4 6DT
Parkstone	Harbour Chandlers	19 Bournemouth Road, BH14 0EF
	Fredk. C. Mitchell & Sons	Sandbanks Road, BH14 8JW
Plymouth	A. E. Monson	Vauxhall Quay, PL4 0DL
	Saltash Yacht Services	43 Bretonside
	Sutton Marine Ltd	Sutton Harbour, PL4 0DW
Poole	J. Looker	82 High Street, BH15 1DD
	J. G. Meakes	P.H.Y.C. Marina, Salterns Way, Lilliput, BH14 8JR
	H. Pipler & Son Ltd	The Quay, BH15 1HF
Ramsgate	Laurestine Ltd	Royal Harbour
	Stuart Marine Services	50A Harbour Parade
Rye	Sea Cruisers	Strand Shipyard, Winchelsea Road, TN31 7EL
Salcombe	Offshore Seachest	Union Street, TQ8 8BZ
	Salcombe Chandlers	19 Fore Street
Shaldon	Brigantine	The Quay, TQ14 0DL
	Mariners Weigh	Dagmar Street
Southampton	Kelvin Hughes Ltd	3 Central Road, Eastern Docks, SO1 1AH
	Camper & Nicholsons Marine Equipment	Royal Crescent Road, SO9 1WB
Southend-on-Sea	Shoreline (Yachtsmen) Ltd	36 Eastern Esplanade
Southsea	Chris Hornsey Chandlery Ltd	152/154 Eastney Road
Topsham	The Foc'sle	32 Fore Street
	Retreat Boatyard Ltd	Exeter Road, EX3 0LS
Totnes	Compass Sailing & Boating Centre	71 High Street
Wareham	Barnard Boats	10 South Street, BH20 4LT
	Ridge Wharf Yacht Centre	
Warsash	Warsash Nautical Bookshop	31 Newton Road, SO3 6FY
Westcliff-on-Sea	Boatacs	833 London Road, SS0 9SY
West Mersea	Wyatt Yacht Chandlery	128 Coast Road

France

Paris	Le Yacht	55 Av de la Grande Armée, 75116 Paris

Eire

Cork	Mizen Books	Main Street, Schull
	Salters Bar	Baltimore
Dublin	Allweather Marine (Ireland) Ltd	Grand Canal Quay (off Pearse St), Dublin 2
	Dublin Boat Centre Ltd	Airport Road, Cloghran
	Perry & Co Ltd	114 Lower George's Street, Dun Loaire
Kerry	O'Sullivans Marine Ltd	Rock Street, Tralee

Stanfords Coloured Charts (Stan) are published by:

Barnacle Marine Ltd, The Wharehouse, 1 Crowhurst Road, Colchester, Essex, CO3 3JN.
They are generally available at most outlets selling BA or Imray charts.

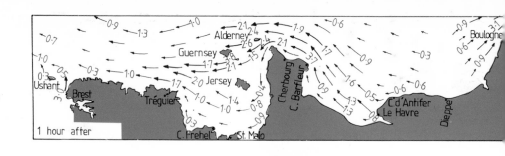

Mean rate of tidal streams in the Channel during the six hours after HW DOVER.

Arrows indicate direction of the stream. The figures give average rate in knots at each point. For Spring rate, add one-third. At Neaps, subtract one-third of the figures shown on each chart.

For greater detail, see Admiralty Tidal Stream Atlases or relevant charts.

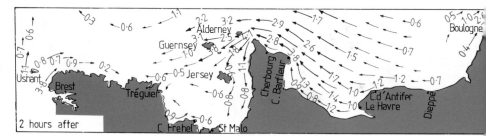

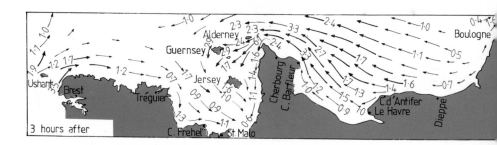